P9-AOM-207

NATURAL HISTORIES

Overleaf: Toulouse-Lautrec's design
for cover of original edition

Histoires

Naturelles

JULES RENARD
NATURAL HISTORIES

TRANSLATED BY RICHARD HOWARD

HORIZON PRESS   NEW YORK

ILLUSTRATED WITH

LITHOGRAPHS AND DRAWINGS BY

Toulouse Lautrec

Bonnard

WStein

COMMENTARY BY EDGAR MUNHALL

TRANSLATOR'S INTRODUCTION

In the mid-eighteenth century, Buffon published his massive *Histoire Naturelle,* which in its sober, enlightened style describes—quite monolithically, when we compare his observations with those of La Fontaine, so evidently drawn *sur le vif*—nothing less than the life of nature on earth, if not always, like the classical fabulist, the nature of life. The man who said "style is the man" accounted, heroically, humorlessly, for the races of animals and birds, working for the most part from stuffed specimens, skins and sketches. His enterprise was pre-eminently mental, rationalizing, deductive; of the falcon, for example, he remarks: "the individual is a slave, only the species is free," and the pre-Darwinian intuition of evolution is a characteristic note sounded by this master of the Age des Lumières, with his ordering, unifying, generalizing impulse toward enclosing structures.

And such a notion of the life of beasts was to stand—illustrated, most recently, by Picasso—as the representative work in the genre until the very end of the nineteenth century, when—in 1896—it was not so much supplanted as disputed by Jules Renard's *Histoires Naturelles,* eventually illustrated by Toulouse-Lautrec and Bonnard. The singular thing about Renard's work from the very start is the plural in the title: there is nothing structural, nothing unifying, nothing monolithic here, but instead a delight taken, an elation shown in the various, the complex, the manifold. Indeed Renard is not

concerned to describe or classify at all, but rather to drama-
tize, to embody, to make exceptional the very characteristics
of life it is usually a matter of systematizing in "natural history"; for Renard, in other words, an animal is real when
there is no other like it; for Buffon, say, an animal is real because it is so painstakingly coherent and lifelike—i.e., dead.

Yet Renard differs just as sharply from later nature-writers
like Colette and D. H. Lawrence, whose method is to identify
themselves with the animal life being observed and described,
to become Other by stripping themselves of their own specifi-
cally human styles. Instead, Renard, whose voice is one of
extreme concision, proceeds to identify the animals with *himself*—the characteristic nineteenth-century touch, I think—
so that the ox or the kingfisher speaks as if, for one lucky
moment, it *were* Jules Renard, though no less ox or kingfisher for all that. What saves such work from being merely
cute or curious is the *intimacy,* the combination of intense
observation and ruthless honesty, in Renard's undertaking.

In manuals of French literature, Jules Renard, the author
of a number of plays, three novels and an enormous journal,
is often referred to as a writer of "autobiographical tendency," and for once the manuals are correct: even these
"natural histories," accounts of the animals, the birds, the
insects, even a few trees and flowers at a single, incised moment of their being, are the accounts of the toad-*as*-Jules
Renard, of the guinea-hen-*as*-Jules Renard, and so on. These
creatures are moments in the writer's biography.

Renard spent a lifetime devising a way of telling the truth
which would be acceptable, even palatable (as so much of his
Journal is not): it was not surprising that he should have
turned to nature and set it speaking—with all possible charm,

8

condensation and wit—in his own voice. For in the history of literature, writers have always turned to animal fables when the truth was too much for them, too much for their society to face out of the mouths of men. Jules Renard crystallizes this tendency, keeping his eyes sharp, his mind free, his ears and nostrils wide, and thereby produces a kind of quintessence of all the fabulists: the world of nature through the sense-assigning lens of one man's senses.

Everything is implicit in these seventy informal pieces, rarely more than a page long (though when we hear them in Ravel's wonderful settings we realize they obey a prosody as strict as it is idiosyncratic), for the very morality by which the world is judged is inherent in the sense-data this "image hunter" accumulates. There are no "morals" at the ends— the morality is in the seeing and hearing itself, not separable from a response to reality, the act of life itself.

Richard Howard

JULES RENARD
HISTOIRES
NATURELLES
DESSINS DE P. BONNARD

Original title page for the book illustrated by Pierre Bonnard

CONTENTS

CONTENTS

HISTOIRES NATURELLES

(the French text in a separate section at the end of this book)

COMMENTARY ON THE ILLUSTRATIONS

"But ask now the beasts, and they shall teach thee;
and the fowls of the air, and they shall tell thee."
(Job. XII, 7)

The origins of the present illustrated translation of Jules Renard's *Histoires Naturelles* appear prosaic: Henri de Toulouse-Lautrec, an experienced illustrator, encounters in 1894 Jules Renard, a leading literary figure and offers to illustrate his recently completed *Natural Histories*. Only five years after the publication of Lautrec's illustrations, the quality of Renard's pungent text provokes Bonnard's very different illustrations for another edition of it. Eventually the aura which these two publications assume, combined with a special naturalistic interest on Walter Stein's part, excite Philip Hofer in 1960 to create a modern American equivalent of these *livres de peintre* in a new publication of excerpts from Renard's text.

In fact the origin both of Renard's text and of the various illustrations before us are distant and richly woven into the fabric of their times. *Natural Histories* have been appearing regularly since antiquity, their content at times being more purely scientific, moralistic or literary according to the outlook of their author. The celebrated "Physiologus" who wrote one, probably in Greek, between the II and V centuries A.D., described forty-five beasts. The innumerable translations of

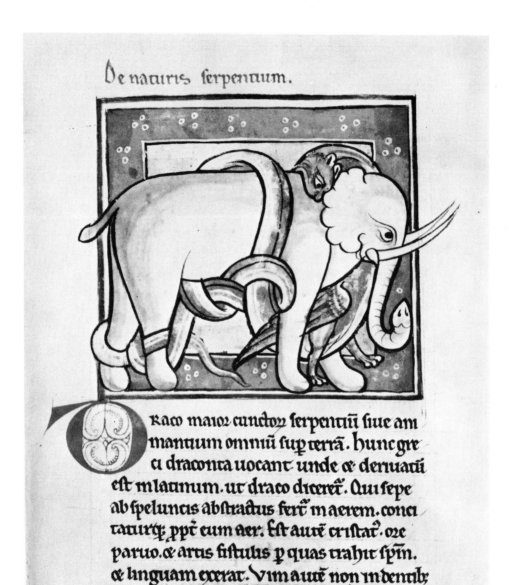

De naturis serpentium.

Raco maior cunctor serpentiu siue am
mantium omniu sup terrā. hunc gre
ci draconta uocant. unde & deriuatu
est in latinum. ut draco dicereē. Qui sepe
ab speluncis abstractus ferē in aerem. concī
taturʒ ppt eum aer. Est autē cristat. oʒe
paruo. & artis fistulis p quas trahit spīn.
& linguam exerat. Vim autē non in dentibʒ

(Fig. 1) "The Serpent," Worksop Bestiary, English, XII Century, The Pierpont Morgan Library, New York *(Photo: Pierpont Morgan Library)*

his work constitute the primary source for the medieval bestiaries—the "naturalists' scrap-books" of the Middle Ages. Among the hundreds of beasts which the bestiaries described were supernatural ones such as the Manticore and Sirens, but these works in fact were seriously attempting to describe nature, and in so doing render praise to the Creator. Moralistic reflections and humorous asides pepper these manuscripts which were lavishly illustrated. "Draco" (The Dragon-serpent) shown strangling an elephant in an English XII century bestiary (Fig. 1) is a typical example. Surely the illustrator had never seen an elephant near his monastery at Lincoln nor such a splendidly long serpent, which another bestiary described as "the biggest of all living things on earth." He depicts Draco's fatal embrace in the manner of a decorative interlace; the forms are simplified into pattern and the image is an integral part of the page. Each bestiary repeats the description of this encounter and each illustrator provides an image of it, the two executing so many variations on a magical theme. Awesome as the serpent's power may have been, the reader was always consoled by its unavoidable self-destruction as the elephant, in collapsing, would inevitably fall down on top of his killer.

Through the poetry of Spenser and Milton, something of the demonic variety of nature recounted in the bestiaries was carried on but only as a background element. The *Fables* of Jean de La Fontaine (1668 and later), with all their crucial antique sources, constitute a new, sophisticated version of the "natural history." A subtle understanding of animal characteristics joined with shrewd observations of human behavior make this work a monument within the wild life genre of literature. In the mid-XVIII century Jean-Baptiste Oudry, already known as the "La Fontaine of painting," produced 276 illustrations for a sumptuous edition of the *Fables* edited by de Montenault. "The Two Adventurers and the Talisman," engraved by Cochin after Oudry's chalk drawing (Fig. 2), demonstrates the transformation that had occurred in naturalistic illustrations. Oudry had seen an elephant in the royal menageries, and drew it as precisely as he did the ducks and frogs of his native Ile-de-France. Specialized as an animal-painter, he regularly received orders to commemorate moments of Louis XV's hunts, or the snarling visages of his dogs in portraits. But in the conception of an illustrated book, his *Fables* are as sensitively designed as the bestiary: illustrations balancing handsome text in a classical, opulent manner.

The flood of anatomical treatises which began with Leonardo da Vinci's dissection of horses and continued in the rich studies of George Stubbs in the XVIII century gained momentum under the scientific aegis of the XIX century. As part of the enthusiastic study of natural life and its possible economic exploitation, private menageries were expanded into municipal zoos, where urban dwellers were able to see their first yak and reflect upon the respective merits of Jersey and Holstein-Friesian cattle.

Toulouse-Lautrec was one person who visited the Parisian zoo called the "Jardin d'Acclimatation" to observe there "foreign plants and animals suitable for domestic or ornamental purposes." His childhood experiences at Malromé, where he painted and drew numerous farm animals, had given him a familiarity with animal life but when he came to execute his final drawings for Renard, many of which are now at the Museum of Albi, he required actual models. He secured a toad, for instance, whose disappearance sent him

LES DEUX AVANTURIERS ET LE TALISMAN . Fable CCII . 2ᵉ planche.

J.B. Oudry inv .

C. Baquoy Sculp

(Fig. 2) "Les Deux Avanturiers et le Talisman," J. B. Oudry's illustration for Jean
de La Fontaine's *Fables*, IV, Paris, 1759   *(Photo: Francis Beaton)*

wandering forlornly after it along the streets of Montmartre; he abandoned his inspiring brothels for the zoos, where he observed that the penguins waddled about much as he did himself. He might even have been given a start in the "Jardin des Plantes" where the skeleton of "Bébé" constituted an attraction signalled out regularly by the Baedeker Guides: it was the favorite dwarf of King Stanislas of Poland, measuring only 27 inches in height.

Lautrec worked on his drawings for a period of three years before the final lithographs were drawn on stone late in 1898 and early in 1899. The Floury edition which appeared that year numbered 100 copies. Lautrec was clearly more interested in familiar, domestic animals than in the ethereal, exotic species which attracted Stein. In his illustrations, Lautrec, like one of Renard's later illustrators, avoids the occasional human character such as Jacquot or Abel who appear in the text. He glorifies through cropped composition the strength and dignity of "The Bull" or "The Buck." This admiration for awesome natural power and sympathy with ordinary animal character recall the prophetic dedication Lautrec's father inscribed in his first gift to his son, a treatise on falconry: "If one day you taste the bitterness of life, the horse above all, then the dog and the falcon may be precious companions for you, helping you to forget a bit . . ." They also recall a lifelong fascination with animal life that first manifested itself when Lautrec was three years old. At the baptism of his brother Richard he offered to draw an ox in lieu of the signature he was incapable of putting in the parish register. There is an undeniable gloom and solemnity to Lautrec's illustrations, culminating in the menacing "Spider" and the dramatic "Sparrow-hawk," which had flesh hanging from its beak and a rabbit in its claws in the artist's original design. And yet Lautrec's invincible wit is evident in the *Natural Histories*. The fox that appears on the previously unpublished book cover (see the frontispiece) is not an animal in Renard's text but rather a visual pun on the author's name, and Lautrec's familiar signature on "The Rabbits" appropriately has rabbit ears.

As a picturesque figure Lautrec fascinated Renard. "The Hunter of Images" spoke frequently of the artist in his *Journal* and seemed genuinely pleased with his illustrations. But the existence of Pierre Bonnard, who executed the much more complete set of sixty-seven illustrations published in 1904, is not alluded to even once. Ending a post-scriptum in a letter written to Paul Cornu shortly after the publication of the Flammarion edition, Renard asked, "would you get me a copy of the illustrated *Histoires Naturelles?*"—not even mentioning the artist's name. The only explanation for this lack of interest seems to be that Bonnard, like Ravel who had composed exquisite songs to the text of some of the *Histoires Naturelles,* was too avant-garde a figure for Renard's more withdrawn and ascetic world. When Ravel invited Renard to hear his compositions, the author declined but sent his wife and daughter.

Working at Etang-la-Ville, at Montval and in the Paris zoos, Bonnard drew with a heavy bristle brush whose rough character dominates so many of his drawings, creating thick black lines which become the tail of "The Magpie" or suggest a deep blue sky. Familiar animals such as his hound "Fachol" appear frequently and with the reduced scale of the artist's designs they contribute an intimacy quite unlike Lautrec's grander vision of Renard's theme. The two artists had known each other since 1895 yet little carries over from the first edition of Renard's text to the second. Just as Lautrec brought Bonnard to a drunken stupor when the young artist joined him in a famous party after a long, healthy walk in the country, so his lithographs overwhelm Bonnard's gentler, sparkling scenes.

In 1900 Bonnard had made something of a splash in the Salon with a portrait of the Terrasse family, a picture whose full title indicates the artist's basic enthusiasm for the world of which Renard had written: "The Terrasse Family, or a Bourgeois Afternoon, with Dogs, Cats, Roosters and Hens in the Dauphionois Landscape of Grand-temps." From 1889 on he regularly exhibited interior scenes and portraits which included dogs and cats, hens and an occasional partridge. Indeed the impression left by Bonnard's immense *oeuvre* is of an exultant fusing of light and form, pulsating with life— whether vegetal, human or animal. His illustrations, such as that of "The Goat" are less dignified than Lautrec's but consequently more truthful. His rendering of the content is usually more precise, as in "The Roosters" where he employs two drawings to oppose the three-dimensional bird to the flat object. More than Lautrec or Stein, Bonnard locates his animals: "The Mouse" in a setting of beams and floor boards, "The Ox" within a barnyard, "The Sparrow-hawk" in a total landscape with trees, houses and the village church. His tendency to open up Renard's text leads Bonnard to include humans—either in part, as with "The Flea," or whole figures, as on his title page (see page 10).

In 1922, the year of Bonnard's retrospective exhibition at the Galerie Druet, his edition of the *Histoires Naturelles* was reprinted and for many years remained the standard form of

Renard's text. His original brush drawings passed into various private collections.

Philip Hofer, who owned some of Lautrec's original sketches for the *Histoires Naturelles,* published seventeen of Lautrec's illustrations in 1954 with his own translations in a thin volume entitled *A Bestiary by Toulouse-Lautrec.* Several years later he met Walter Stein who had published in 1956 *A Common Botany* with drawings of spiders and other insects. The encounter led to a new illustrated edition of parts of Renard's text published by the Department of Printing and Graphic Arts of Harvard College Library, which the artist worked on in late 1959 and early 1960. Reading through Renard's text Stein chose the subjects which interested him, admittedly preferring those equipped with the shortest text and so requiring less labor of translation—such as "Monkeys. . . ." Hofer then translated the appropriate passages of Renard's text for publication. Originally Hofer and Stein planned simply to reproduce the drawings but later the idea of an edition combining original lithographs with offset reproductions seemed more attractive. No longer using the stone plates of Lautrec's time, Stein first experimented with aluminum and zinc ones and later paper plates, printed by offset. The size of the plate required executing eight perfectly satisfactory drawings on it, a challenge which Stein met only after innumerable trial drawings. Through accidents some of the plates were lost and had to be remade several times. At the time of publication in 1960 Stein's original drawings, done in pencil on Rives paper, were shown at Durlacher Bros. and are now in various American collections.

Lacking the rural experience of Lautrec and Bonnard, Stein tended to concentrate on the animals available to him in

(Fig. 3) Mounted Cricket, Collection Walter Stein, New York (*Photo: Francis Beaton*)

zoos. New York's Central Park Zoo provided him with his "Monkeys . . ." and "The Elephant," among others, while the Bronx Zoo housed "The Pelican" and "The Donkey." Kirk Askew's cow, his dog "Sadie" and cat "Peanut" posed, and scientific supply houses provided models for most of the insects, such as "The Cricket" (Model. Fig. 3).

Despite the scientific air of Stein's preparations, his illustrations are certainly the gentlest and most immaterial of the three. His sympathies are clearly with the insects, whose fragile composite structures and shimmering appendages are most suited to his style. He uses cropped compositions somewhat in the manner of Lautrec but more to suggest intimacy with the animal, such as "The Dog," than to create a scale larger than life. His "Toad" is a deliberate pastiche of Lautrec's, but with gentler eyes and a quivering mouth. Perhaps Stein's "Lion" is his most characteristic illustration: the classic zoo beast has become a domestic creature.

Like the ancient bestiaries these three sets of illustrations reveal to us different aspects of Renard's basic text, each suggesting feelings which move one man but not another. It is not that one artist reaches closer towards the essence of the *Natural Histories*. Lautrec, Bonnard and Stein each expose an equally valid aspect of Renard's work and in doing so expose themselves even more. So often illustrations only annoy us in their obvious failure to equal the quality of the text, let alone heighten it, but with the *Natural Histories* we are almost left with the embarrassing situation of preferring them.

Edgar Munhall
Curator, The Frick Collection

ILLUSTRATIONS

[Abbreviations: L. (Lautrec), B. (Bonnard), S. (Stein). *The numbers refer to the pages on which the illustrations by each of the artists may be found.]*

NATURAL HISTORIES

THE IMAGE HUNTER

He jumps out of bed early in the morning and sets out only if his mind is clear, his heart pure, his body light as a summer shirt. He takes no provisions. He will drink the fresh air *en route*, feed on the good smells. He leaves all his weapons at home and merely keeps his eyes open; *they* will trap the images.

The first one caught is the image of the road, which exposes its bones, smooth pebbles, and its ruts, popped veins, between two hedges covered with sloes and blackberries.

Then he captures the image of the river. It pales around its bends and sleeps under the willow's caress. It shimmers when a fish turns up its belly, as if someone had thrown in a coin, and as soon as the rain starts—even a shower—the river has gooseflesh.

He collects images of the shifting wheat, the appetizing alfalfa, and the fields hemmed with streams. He manages to bag, in passing, the flight of a lark, or of a goldfinch.

Then he enters the woods. He didn't know his senses were so delicate. Soon impregnated by perfumes, he does not miss the faintest murmur, and in order to communicate with the trees, his veins branch into the veins of leaves.

Soon, quivering almost uncomfortably, he perceives too much, he *ferments*, he is frightened, leaves the woods and follows—at a distance—some workmen returning to the village.

Outside, he gazes a moment, until his eyes explode, at the low sun stripping off its luminous garments, its clouds scattered pell-mell on the horizon.

Finally, home again, his head crammed, he turns out the light and for a long time, before falling asleep, tallies his images, his trophies.

Docile, they reappear at memory's command. Each of them wakens another, and their phosphorescent horde keeps swelling with newcomers, like partridges that, hunted and scattered by day, sing all night, safe from harm, calling to each other from the dark furrows.

THE HEN

Feet together, she jumps down from the coop, as soon as the door is opened.

An ordinary fowl, modestly adorned, that has never once laid a golden egg.

Dazed by the light, she takes a few undecided steps in the barnyard.

First thing she sees is the ashheap where she is in the habit of taking a bath every morning.

She rolls in it until she is covered, then with a quick flutter of wings, feathers puffed, shakes off the night's fleas.

Then she goes over to the shallow dish the last rainstorm has filled, and takes a drink.

She drinks nothing but water.

36

She drinks in tiny sips, straightening her neck each time, balancing on the edge of the dish.

Then she looks around for her scattered food.

The little weeds are hers, and the insects, and the stray seeds.

She pecks, she pecks, tirelessly.

From time to time, she stops.

Upright under her Phrygian cap, eyes quick, her jabot becoming, she listens, first with one ear, then the other.

And convinced there is nothing new, she begins searching again.

She raises her stiff feet high, like someone with the gout. She spreads her toes and sets them down carefully, without a sound.

As if she were walking barefoot.

Coqs

ROOSTERS

I

He has never crowed. He has never spent a night in the henhouse, or known a single hen.

He is made out of wood, with an iron foot coming out of the middle of his belly, and for years and years he has lived on top of an old church, the kind no one dares build any more. It looks like a barn, in fact, and the ridge of its slates makes a line as straight as an ox's back.

And now some masons have appeared at the other end of the church.

The wooden rooster looks at them, until a sudden gust of wind forces him to turn his back.

And each time he veers around, new stones block out a little more of his horizon.

Soon, jerking his head up, he notices, on the steeple they have just completed, a young cockerel that was not there this morning. The stranger carries his tail high, opens his beak like the kind that crow, and with his wings on his hips, brand-new, glistens in the sun.

At first the two roosters compete, whirling around. But the old wooden cock is soon exhausted and surrenders. Under his single foot, the pole threatens collapse. He leans stiffly, about to fall. He creaks and stops.

Here come the carpenters.

They knock through this wormeaten corner of the church, take down the rooster and parade him through the village. Anyone can touch him, for a present.

Someone gives an egg, someone else a penny, and Madame Loriot a silver coin.

The carpenters have a few drinks, and after a quarrel over the rooster they decide to burn him.

Having made him a nest of sticks and straw, they set fire to it.

The wooden rooster crackles loudly, and his flames rise to the heaven he has certainly reached.

II

Every morning, jumping from the perch, the rooster looks to see if the other one is still there—and the other one always is.

The rooster crows over and over: he calls, provokes, threatens—but the other one answers only in his own good time, and at first does not answer at all.

The rooster preens, puffs his feathers, which are not bad—some blue, some silvery—but the other one, up against the sky, is gleaming gold.

The rooster collects his hens and walks at the head of the line. Look: they are his, they all love him, fear him—but the other one is worshipped by swallows.

The rooster outdoes himself: here and there he sets a grace note, and triumphs, shrilly, over a whole cascade of crotchets—but it so happens the other one is getting married and chimes out his village wedding, peal after peal.

The jealous rooster spurs himself on to a supreme combat; his tail looks like the hem of a cloak raised by a sword. He defies all the cocks of heaven, his crest swollen with blood—but the other one, who is not afraid to challenge even the storm winds, is playing with the breeze at this moment, and turns his back.

And the rooster rages until sunset.

His hens go in, one by one. He remains alone, hoarse, flouted, in the already dark barnyard—but the other one still glistens in the last rays of the sun, and in his pure voice sings out the calm evening angelus.

Canards

DUCKS

She comes first, limping on both feet, to dabble in a hole she knows about.

The drake follows her. Wingtips crossed over his back, he limps on both feet too.

And duck and drake walk on, taciturn as though to a board meeting.

She slithers down ahead of him into the muddy water in which feathers, droppings, a grape leaf and some straws are floating. She has almost vanished.

She is waiting. She is ready.

And the drake enters in his turn. He drowns his rich colors. All you can see is his green head and the kiss-curls of his behind. Here, they are both comfortable. The water keeps them warm. It's never drained, and changed only on rainy days.

The drake, with his flattened bill, nibbles and squeezes the back of her neck. For a moment he shakes himself, and the water is so thick with mud that it scarcely trembles. And soon calm again, quite smooth, it reflects, blackly, a sliver of cloudless sky.

Duck and drake are no longer moving. The sun bakes them, puts them to sleep. You might come quite close without noticing them. They betray themselves only by the rare bubbles that rise and burst on the stagnant surface.

THE GOOSE

Tiennette would love to go to Paris, like the other girls in the village. But can she even take care of her geese?

As a matter of fact, she follows them rather than leads. She does her knitting, mechanically, behind their troupe, and leaves matters up to the Toulouse goose that knows as much as any grownup.

The Toulouse goose knows the way, the best grass, and when it is time to go home.

Braver than the gander himself, she protects her sisters against the barking dog. Her neck quivers and snakes along

the ground, then straightens until she towers over the paralyzed Tiennette. Once everything is all right, she shows off and sings, through her nose, who is responsible for restoring order.

She has no doubt she could do even better.

And one evening, she leaves the region.

She walks off down the road, bill high, feathers pasted flat. The women she happens to meet dare not stop her. She walks so fast it's intimidating.

And while Tiennette, left behind, grows stupider every day, until you can't tell her from the rest of the geese, the Toulouse goose comes to Paris.

49

La Dinde

THE TURKEY-HEN

I

She struts through the barnyard in state, as if she were living under the *ancien régime*.

The other fowls do nothing but eat all the time, whatever they can find. But she, between her regular meals, is concerned only with looking her best. All her feathers are starched, and her wingtips score the earth, as though to trace the path she takes: it is *here* that she is walking and not elsewhere.

She swaggers so much, breast distended, that she never sees her feet.

She suspects no one, and as I approach she supposes I intend to pay my respects.

Already she is gobbling complacently.

"Noble Creature," I remark, "if you were a goose, I'd indite your praises as Buffon did, with one of your quills. But you're only a turkey-hen."

I must have annoyed her, for the blood rushes to her head. Grapes of wrath hang from her beak. She has a fit of red. With a dry click, she opens the fan of her tail, and this old prude turns her back on me.

II

Out on the road, here are the turkey-hens again, a whole boarding-school of them.

Every day, whatever the weather, they take their constitutional.

They pay no attention to the rain—no one tucks up her skirts better than a turkey-hen; nor to the sun—a turkey-hen never goes outdoors without her parasol.

La Pintade

THE GUINEA HEN

She is the hunchback of my barnyard. The only thing she can think of is quarrelling—because of her hump.

The hens have nothing to do with her, and all of a sudden she goes for them like a fury. Then she lowers her head, leans forward, and as fast as her skinny feet can carry her, she dashes over and pecks—hard—at the very center of a turkey-cock's fantail.

If there's one thing she can't stand it's affectation.

That's how it is: from morning to night she fumes on, head blue, wattles stiff with rage. She picks fights for no reason, maybe because she imagines they're making fun of her size, her bald head and her runty tail.

And she keeps making her harsh little cry that stabs the air like another beak.

Sometimes she leaves the barnyard and disappears, affording the peaceful fowl there a moment's relief. But she returns more turbulent and noisier than ever. In a frenzy, she sprawls on the ground.

What's the matter with her now?

The sneak is up to something.

She's gone off to lay her egg in the field somewhere.

I can go hunt for it if I want to.

She rolls around in the dust, like a hunchback.

Les Pigeons

THE PIGEONS

Even though they make a noise like muffled drums on the roof;

Even though they emerge from the shadows, turn somersaults, explode in the sunshine and return to the shadows;

Even though their fugitive throats live and die like the opal on your finger;

Even though they fall asleep in the woods, at night, squeezed so close together that the topmost branch of the oak threatens to crack under its load of painted fruit;

Even though these two are exchanging frenzied greetings and abruptly, one after the other, break into convulsions;

Even though this one returns from exile, with a letter, and flies like thoughts of our faraway love (Ah, a pledge!)—

All these pigeons, which are entertaining enough at first, turn out to be a bore.

They don't know how to keep still, and travel hasn't broadened them at all.

They remain a little stupid all their lives.

They persist in thinking one has children because of something one does with one's beak.

And in the long run, who can stand their hereditary mania for always having something stuck in their throats?

The Two Pigeons: "Coo, Love! . . . Coo, Love! . . . Coo, Love! . . ."

L'Ane

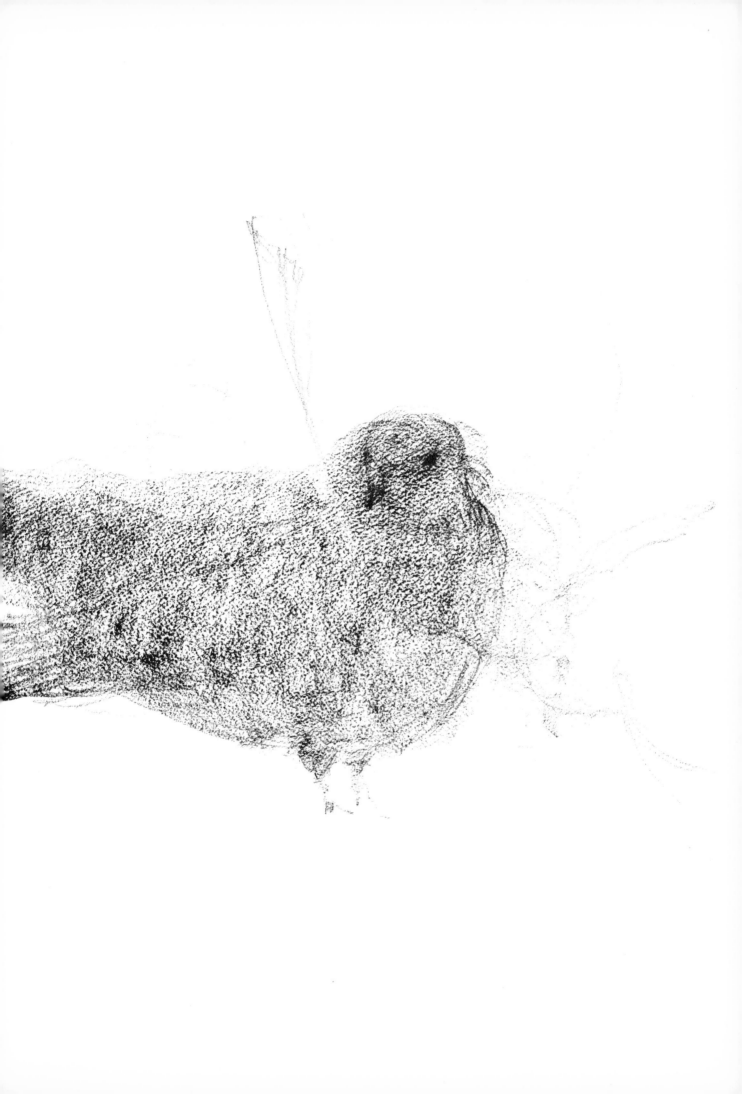

Le

Paon

THE PEACOCK

He must be getting married today.

It was supposed to be yesterday. Wearing his best, he was ready. All he was waiting for was his fiancée. She didn't come. She can't be long now.

Superb, he strolls about as indolently as any Hindu prince, and bears upon himself the rich ceremonial presents. Life enlivens the luster of his colors, and his crest trembles like a lyre.

The fiancée does not come.

He climbs to the roof and looks toward the sun. He utters his diabolic cry:

Léon! Léon!

That is what he calls his fiancée. He sees nothing coming, and no one answers. The hens, accustomed, do not even raise their heads. They are tired of admiring him. He comes back down into the barnyard, so sure of being beautiful that he is incapable of rancor.

The marriage will take place tomorrow.

And undecided about what to do with the rest of the day, he heads for the terrace in front of the house. He climbs the steps as though they were temple steps, with an official gait.

He raises his train that is so heavy with the eyes which could not tear themselves away.

And once more he repeats the ceremony.

Le
Cygne

THE SWAN

He slides across the pond like a white sled, from cloud to cloud. You see, that's all he likes to eat: the cottony clouds he watches appearing, moving, and vanishing in the water. It's one of them he wants. He aims at it with his beak, and abruptly plunges his snowy neck into it.

Then, the way a woman's arm comes out of a sleeve, he withdraws it.

He has nothing.

He stares: the startled clouds have vanished.

His disappointment lasts only a moment, for the clouds don't take long to come back, and over there, where the ripples are dying out, one is forming again.

Gently, on his light cushion of feathers, the swan rows over to it...

He wears himself out fishing for vain reflections, and perhaps he will starve, a victim of this illusion, before he catches a single piece of cloud.

But what am I saying?

Each time he dives, he pokes his beak into the nourishing mud and brings up a worm.

He's getting fat as a goose.

Le Chien

THE DOG

We can't put Pointu outside in weather like this, and even
the icy draught under the door forces him to leave his mat.
He looks for something warmer, and slides his smooth head
between our chairs. But we are sitting close together, elbow
to elbow, around the fire, and I give Pointu a slap. My father
pushes him away with one foot. Maman insults him. My
sister holds out an empty glass.

Pointu sneezes and goes out to the kitchen to see if we're
there.

Then he returns, forces his way into the circle, at the risk
of being strangled by knees, and now he's in a corner of the
fireplace.

After circling in the same place for a long time, he sits
down near the andirons and doesn't move again. He glances
at his masters, eyes so gentle that we tolerate him. Only, the
almost red-hot andiron and the scattered ashes are scorching
his behind.

He stays, all the same.

We make room for him:

"Here, get out, stupid!"

But he doesn't budge. At the hour when the teeth of all
lost dogs are chattering, Pointu, warm as toast, hair smoking,
hindquarters roasted, swallows his howls and merely pants
a little, his eyes full of tears . . .

THE CAT

Mine never eats mice; he doesn't like them. He only catches one now and then to play with it.

When he has played enough, he lets the mouse off with his life and goes to sleep somewhere else, innocently sitting in the loop of his tail, head closed tight as a fist.

But because of his claws, the mouse is dead.

THE COW

Tired of trying to think one up, we ended by not giving her a name.

She is called, simply, "the cow" and it's the name that suits her best.

Besides, what difference does it make, provided she can eat!

And now, the fresh grass, the hay, the vegetables, the wheat, even bread and salt—she has it all, whenever she wants, and she eats it all, all the time, even twice, since she ruminates.

As soon as she sees me, she runs up, light on her split hooves, skin drawn smooth as a white stocking over her legs, convinced I am bringing her something to eat. And admiring her each time, I can only say, "Here, eat this!"

But out of what she absorbs, she makes milk, not fat. At the appointed hour she offers her full, square udder. She doesn't hold back her milk—there are cows that do—but generously, through her four elastic teats, barely squeezed, she empties her cistern. She does not stir her feet or her tail, but with her enormous supple tongue she enjoys licking the milkmaid's back.

Although she lives alone, her appetite keeps her from getting bored. It's rare that she lows, regretfully, at the vague memory of her last calf. But she enjoys visits, graciously holding her horns high, her lips eager, and from them dangling, always, a thread of water and a wisp of hay.

The men of the farm, who fear nothing, smack her swelling belly; the women, amazed that so huge an animal should be so gentle, no longer shrink except from her caresses, and begin to count on a good profit from the next calf.

She likes me to scratch between her horns. I move back a little, because the pleasure draws her forward, and the good creature lets me keep on until I've stepped into her latest cowpat.

THE DEATH OF BRUNETTE

Philippe wakens me, saying that he got up in the night to listen, and that her breathing was calm.

But since this morning, she's been worrying him.

He gives her hay and she won't eat it. He offers her a little fresh grass, and Brunette, usually so fond of treats, scarcely touches it. She no longer looks at her calf and doesn't like it poking at her when it stands on its stiff legs to nurse.

Philippe separates them and ties the calf far from its mother. Brunette doesn't seem to notice.

Philippe's anxiety spreads to the rest of us. Even the children want to get up.

The veterinary arrives, examines Brunette, and makes her walk out of the barn. She knocks against the wall and stumbles over the doorstep. She would fall down; we have to bring her back.

"She's very sick," the veterinary says.

We don't dare ask what it is.

He's afraid it's a milk fever, often fatal, especially to good milkers, and recalling one by one the cows he thought doomed that he has managed to save, he brushes the liquid from a little bottle over Brunette's flanks.

"It will act as a vesicatory," he says. "I'm not even sure of the exact formula. It comes from Paris. If the trouble doesn't reach her head, she'll get over it by herself, if not I'll try ice-water. It sometimes comes as a surprise to the farmers around here, but I know what I'm talking about."

"Do whatever you can, Monsieur."

Brunette, lying on the straw, can still hold up her head. She's stopped chewing her cud. She seems to be holding her breath to hear what's happening inside her.

We wrap her in a blanket, because her horns and ears are getting cold.

"Until the ears droop," Philippe says, "there's hope."

Twice she tries to get on her feet. She breathes hard, at longer and longer intervals.

And then she drops her head onto her left side.

"That's a bad sign," Philippe says, crouching and murmuring encouragement to her.

The head comes up again, and is laid on the edge of the manger, so heavily that the muffled impact makes us exclaim: Oh!

We line Brunette with heaps of straw so she won't hurt herself.

She stretches out her neck and legs, makes herself as long as she can, the way she does in the field, in stormy weather.

The veterinary decides to bleed her. He doesn't get too close. He knows as much as anyone, but he seems less brave than some.

At the first taps of the wooden mallet, the lancet slides over the vein. After a more confident blow, the blood spurts out into the pewter pail that the milk usually fills to the brim.

To stop the jet, the veterinary puts a steel pin into the vein.

Then, covering Brunette from her relieved forehead to her tail, we apply a sheet dipped in the well and frequently renewed because it gets warm almost at once. She doesn't even shiver. Philippe holds her fast by the horns and keeps the head from dropping onto the left flank again.

Brunette, as though overcome, no longer moves. We don't know if she's better or worse.

The rest of us are sad, but Philippe's sadness is grim, like the sadness of an animal that has seen another animal suffering.

His wife brings him his morning soup, which he eats without an appetite, on a stool, and which he does not finish.

"It's the end," he says. "She's blowing up."

We doubt this at first, but Philippe was right. Brunette swells even as we watch, and the swelling does not subside, as if the air in her could not get back out.

Philippe's wife asks:

"Is she dead?"

"Can't you see!" Philippe says harshly.

Mme. Philippe goes out into the barnyard.

"I'm not going to be in any hurry to go out and look for another one around here," Philippe says.

"Another what?"

"Another Brunette."

"You'll go when I tell you to," I say in a voice of authority that startles me.

We try to convince ourselves that the accident has given us more irritation than pain, and already we remind ourselves that Brunette is dead and gone.

But this evening I met the bellringer of the church, and I don't know what kept me from saying:

"Here are a hundred sous, go ring the passing-bell for someone in my house who's dead."

Le Bœuf

THE OX

The door opens this morning, as usual, and Castor leaves the stable, without butting against it. In slow mouthfuls he drinks his share from the bottom of the trough and leaves the rest for Pollux, the late-comer. Then, muzzle dripping like a tree after the rain, he walks over to his usual place—dutiful, ponderous, amiable—under the wagon's yoke.

Horns tied, head motionless, he puckers the skin of his belly, lazily slaps his tail at the black flies and, like a maid dozing with the broom in her hand, ruminates while he waits for Pollux.

But out in the barnyard, the bustling farmhands shout and swear; the dog yelps as though a stranger were approaching.

Can it be the docile Pollux who for the first time is resisting the goad, turning around, bumping Castor's side, steaming, and, although harnessed, still trying to shake off the double yoke?

No, it's another one.

Castor, mismatched, stops his jaws when he sees, close to his own, this cloudy bull's eye he doesn't recognize.

As the sun sets, the oxen trudge across the fields, dragging the weightless plow of their shadow.

THE WATER FLIES

There is only one oak tree in the middle of the field, and the cows take up all the shade of its leaves.

Heads down, their horns make the sign of the evil eye at the sun.

They would be all right if it weren't for the flies.

But today, they're biting terribly. Pungent and countless, the black ones cling in patches of sweat to the eyes, the nostrils, even the corners of the lips, and the green ones prefer to suck at the latest scratch.

When a cow twitches her skin, or stamps her hoof on the dry ground, the cloud of flies changes position with a murmur. As if they were fermenting.

It is so hot that the old women, at their doorway, sniff the storm and already they're joking, fearfully:

"Watch out for the lightning," they say.

In the distance, a first luminous spear-thrust pierces the sky, without a sound. One drop of rain falls.

The cows, warned, raise their heads, move right next to the oak and sigh, patiently.

They know: now the good flies are coming to drive away the bad ones.

Infrequent at first, one by one, then in hordes, all together, they fall out of the torn sky upon the enemy which gradually gives way, thins out, disperses completely.

Soon, from flat nose to unusable tail, the streaming cows ripple with delight under the victorious swarm of water flies.

Le Taureau

THE BULL

The fisherman walks gaily along the Yonne, and casts his green fly on the water.

He catches the green flies on the trunks of the poplars that have been polished by cattle rubbing against them.

He casts his fly with a dry snap of the wrist, and reels it in skillfully.

He supposes that each new spot is the best one, and soon leaves it, stepping over a stile, and from this field passes into the next.

Suddenly, as he is crossing a huge, sun-baked pasture, he stops.

Over there, among the peaceful cows lying under a tree, the bull has just stood up, heavily.

It is a famous bull, and his size amazes people passing on the road. They admire him, from a distance, and if he hasn't done as much already, he could send this man high in the air, like an arrow, with the bow of his horns. Milder than a lamb when he feels like it, he is subject to sudden fits of anger: you never know what will happen when you are around him.

The fisherman watches him out of the corner of his eye.

"If I run," he thinks, "the bull will be on me before I get out of the pasture. If I jump into the river, I'll drown. If I play dead here on the ground, the bull is supposed to sniff at me and leave me alone. How can I be sure? And what if he doesn't go away? Better to put up a show of all the indifference I can muster."

And the fisherman goes on casting, as if the bull wasn't there. He hopes, in this way, to deceive him.

Under his straw hat, the nape of his neck is roasting.

He controls his feet, that are itching to run, and forces them to linger on the grass. He has the occasional heroism to cast his green fly on the water. He hides only now and then, behind the poplars. Sedately, he reaches the next hedge-stile, from which, with a final effort of his cramped limbs, he could leap out of the pasture, safe and sound.

Besides, what's his hurry?

The bull is paying no attention to him, and remains with the cows.

He has only stood up to stretch his legs, out of weariness.

He turns his frizzy head to the evening breeze.

He bellows at intervals, eyes half-closed.

He lows languorously, for his own enjoyment.

Women recognize him by the curly hair on his forehead.

99

Le

Cheval

THE HORSE

My horse is anything but handsome. He has too many knots and hollows, flat sides, a rat-tail and buck teeth. But he touches me. I can't get over the fact that he remains at my service, and without once objecting lets himself be turned this way and that, back and forth, and back again.

Each time I harness him, I expect him to tell me: *No*, with a sudden gesture, and clear out.

Not at all. He lowers and lifts his huge head as though to put on a lead hat, obediently steps back between the shafts.

As a matter of fact, there's no limit to the oats and corn I give him. I brush him until his coat glistens like a cherry. I comb out his mane, braid his skimpy tail. I caress him with my hands, my voice. I wipe out his eyes, wax his hooves.

Does this touch *him*?

Who knows.

He farts.

It's particularly when we take out the carriage that I admire him. I crack the whip and he breaks into a trot. I shout *whoa*! and he stops. I pull the left rein and he turns left, instead of going to the right and knocking me into the ditch with a kick somewhere into the bargain.

He frightens me, shames me, makes me feel sorry for him.

Won't he wake up from his half-sleep someday, and boldly taking my place, reduce me to his?

What is he thinking about?

He farts, farts, farts.

THE DONKEY

It's all the same to him. Every morning, always at a quick trot, he pulls the cart of Jacquot the postman, who distributes to the villages the purchases made in town—groceries, bread, meat from the butcher, some newspapers, a letter.

Once these rounds are done, Jacquot and the donkey work on their own. The cart becomes a wagon. They go together to the vineyards, the woods, the potato-fields. They bring back vegetables, sometimes green faggots, other things—it depends on the day.

Jacquot keeps saying: "Hue! hue!" without any reason, as if he was snoring. Now and then the donkey, because of a thistle he smells, or an idea he gets in his head, stops walking. Then Jacquot puts an arm around his neck and pushes. If the donkey resists, Jacquot bites his ear.

They eat in ditches at the roadside, the master a piece of bread and some onions, the animal whatever turns up.

They don't come home before evening. Their shadows pass slowly from one tree to the next.

Suddenly the lake of silence in which things are already steeping is split apart:

Drawing water at this hour? What farmer's wife is pulling up buckets by a rusty, creaking winch?

It is the donkey on his way home, flinging his voice into the night at the top of his lungs, braying to extinction that he couldn't care less, he couldn't care less, he couldn't care . . .

Donkey: The rabbit writ large.

Le Cochon

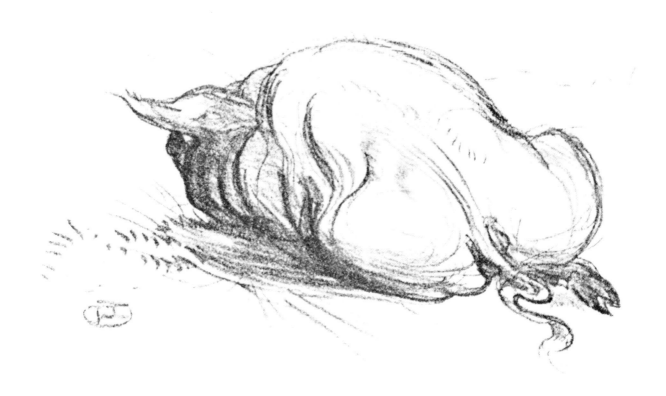

THE HOG

Peevish but intimate as if we had raised you in the house, you stick your snout everywhere, and use it as much as your feet to walk with.

You conceal your tiny black-currant eyes under beet-leaf ears.

You're pot-bellied as a gooseberry.

You have the same long hairs, the same light skin, and a short, tight-curled tail.

And the nasty-minded call you "piggish."

They say that if nothing disgusts you, you disgust everyone else, and that the only thing you like is dishwater—dirty dishwater at that.

But it's a libel.

Properly cleaned up, you'd look pretty enough.

It's their fault if you neglect yourself.

Since they make your bed, you lie in it, and slovenliness is only *second* nature to you.

THE SWINE AND THE PEARLS

As soon as we let him into the pasture, the hog begins eating, and his snout never leaves the ground.

He doesn't seek out the best grass. He attacks whatever comes first and pushes his indefatigable nose in front of him like a ploughshare or a blind mole.

The only thing that concerns him is to fill out a belly that already looks like a salting-tub, and he never bothers about the weather.

What does it matter if his bristles almost catch fire in the noonday sun, or if a heavy hail-swollen cloud is spreading over the pasture now, about to burst?

The magpie, of course, escapes, with her bursts of automatic flight; the turkey-hens hide in the hedge, and the boyish colt takes shelter under an oak.

But the hog stays where he eats.

He doesn't miss a mouthful.

He doesn't move even his tail.

Riddled with hailstones, he barely has time to grunt: "More of their damn pearls."

Les

Moutons

THE SHEEP

They're coming back from the stubble-fields, where they've been grazing since this morning, noses in the shade of their bodies.

Obeying the gestures of a lazy shepherd, the necessary dog attacks the flock wherever it needs attention.

The flock takes up the whole road, undulates from one ditch to the other and overflows; or else, squeezed together, velvety, level, marks time with the tiny steps of old women. When the flock begins running, the hooves make the sound of reeds, and honeycomb the dust of the road.

This curly sheep, filled to bursting, bounces like a tennis-ball, and gumdrops escape from the cornucopia of his ear.

This one has vertigo, and his knee keeps bumping into a head that isn't screwed on tight.

They invade the village. Apparently today is their holiday, and with a certain petulance, they bleat–joyfully, though–through the streets.

But they don't stop in the village, and I see them reappear farther on. They reach the horizon. Over the hill they rise, lighter than air, toward the sun. They approach it, and lie down a little ways off . . .

Laggards, silhouetted against the sky, take a final unexpected form, and rejoin the wadded flock.

One tuft comes loose again and soars, white cotton, smoke, vapor, then nothing . . .

Nothing is left outside now but one foot.

It grows longer, shreds out like the wool on a spindle . . . to infinity.

The chilly sheep fall asleep around the weary sun, which dismantles its crown and until tomorrow sticks its rays in their wool.

The sheep: Bu-u-ut . . . Bu-u-ut . . . Bu-u-ut . . .
The sheepdog: No buts about it!

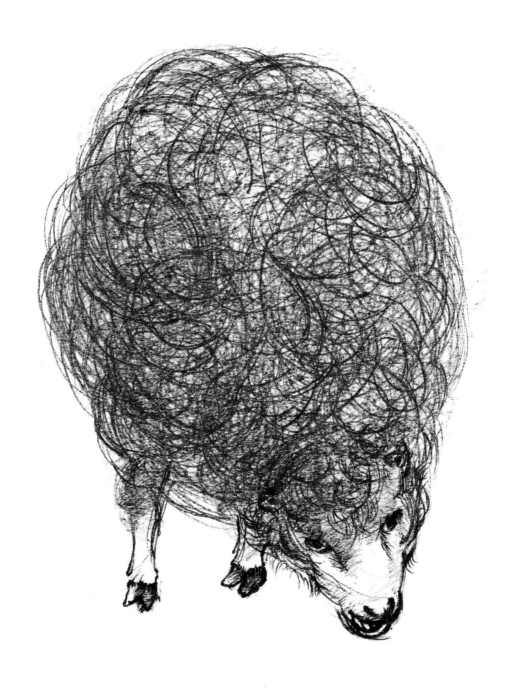

Le
Bouc

THE GOAT

His smell precedes him. He isn't in sight yet, but *it* has arrived.

He leads the flock, and the kids follow, pell-mell, in a cloud of dust.

He has long dry hairs parted down his back.

He is less proud of his beard than of his height, for the nanny-goat also wears a beard under her chin.

When he passes, some people hold their noses, others like that particular odor.

He looks neither to the right nor left: he walks stiffly, ears pointed, tail short. If men have burdened him with their sins, he hasn't heard about it, and merely releases, quite solemnly, a little rosary of droppings.

Alexandre is his name, known even to the dogs.

At the day's end, once the sun has gone down, he returns to the village with the harvesters, and his horns, sagging with age, gradually assume the curve of sickles.

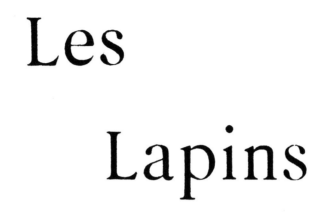

Les
Lapins

THE RABBITS

In a hutch made of half a barrel, Lenoir and Legris, feet warm under their fur, eat like cows. They have only one meal which lasts all day.

If you take too long about throwing them a fresh stalk, they eat the old one down to the root, and even the root keeps their teeth busy.

Now a head of lettuce has fallen to them; together Lenoir and Legris set to work.

Nose to nose they do their best, heads bobbing, ears trotting to keep up.

When only one leaf is left, they each take one end and begin a race.

You'd think they were playing—except that they don't laugh—and once the leaf was swallowed, a brotherly caress would unite their muzzles.

But Legris suddenly weakens. Since yesterday, his belly has been swollen, ballooning with a pocket of water. As a matter of fact, he has overeaten. A leaf of lettuce should be easy enough to get down, even without being hungry, but he can't manage it. He drops the leaf and lies down on his side, right there in the droppings, suffering brief convulsions.

Now he is quite stiff, feet apart, as though on a gunsmith's signboard: *A Clean Shot.*

For a moment, Lenoir stops, surprised. Sitting up, breathing softly, lips together and eyes pink-rimmed, he stares.

He looks like a wizard solving some occult mystery.

His two straight ears mark the supreme moment.

Then they fall back.

And he finishes the lettuce leaf.

La Souris

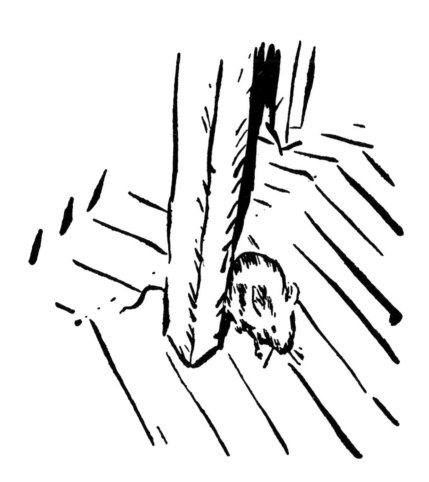

THE MOUSE

As I sit under the lamp, writing out my daily page, I hear a faint noise. If I stop, it stops too. It begins again, as soon as I scratch my way across the paper.

It is a mouse waking up.

I sense her comings and going around the dark corner where the maid keeps her rags and brushes.

The mouse jumps onto the floor and trots across the kitchen tiles. She passes near the fireplace, under the sink, vanishes into the dishes, and by a series of reconnaissance missions which she extends farther and farther, approaches me.

Each time I set down my pen, the silence alarms her. Each time I use it, she thinks, I suppose, that there is another mouse somewhere, and this reassures her.

Then I lose sight of her. She is under my table, at my feet. She circulates from one chair leg to the next. She brushes against my shoes, nibbles the sole, or, boldly, gets up on top!

And now I must not move my leg, or breathe too hard: she would vanish.

But I have to go on writing, or else she would abandon me to my solitude—I write, I doodle, little things, tiny, dainty, the way she nibbles.

THE WEASEL

Poor but very clean, even distinguished, she hurries back and forth across the road, taking tiny hops from one ditch to the other, giving her private lessons from hole to hole.

THE LIZARD

Spontaneous scion of the cracked wall I'm leaning against, he clings to my shoulder, imagining I'm part of the wall because I don't move and because my raincoat is the same color. It's a kind of flattery, even so.

Wall: What was that? A shudder just ran over my back.
Lizard: It's me.

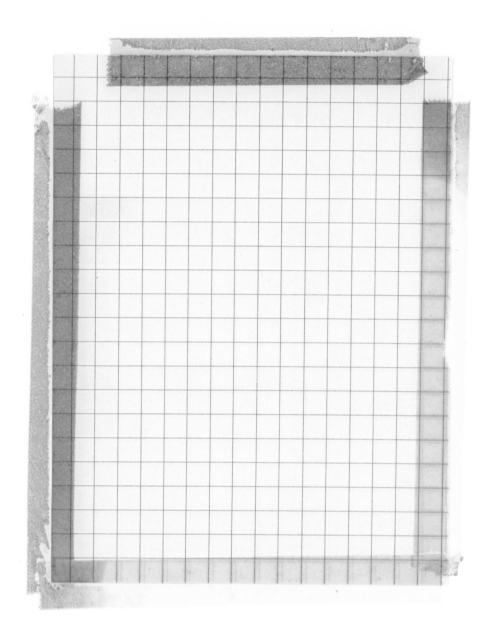

THE WORM

And here's one that stretches and extends like a beautiful noodle.

THE GLOW-WORM

What's going on? Nine o'clock and there's still a light on up there!

THE VIPER

Now what belly did this colic fall out of?

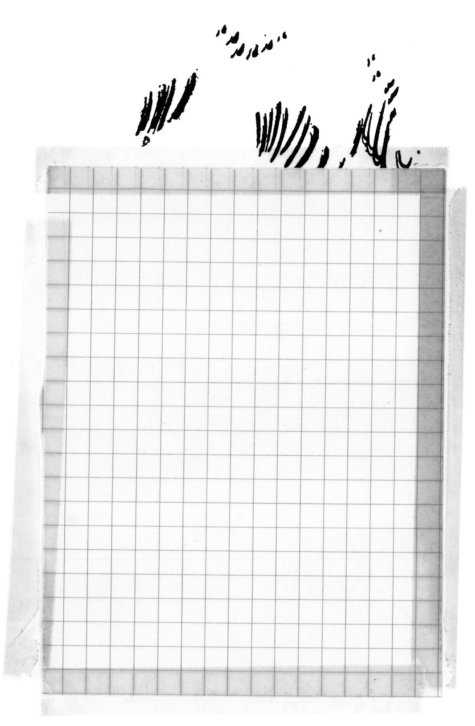

THE SNAKE

Too long.

L'Escargot

THE SNAIL

I

Stay-at-home in the season when everyone has a cold, his giraffe-neck pulled in, the snail seethes like a stuffed nose.

He takes himself for walks as soon as the nice weather comes, but he can only walk on his own tongue.

II

My little friend Abel played with his snails.

He is raising a whole boxful, and he made sure he would recognize them by numbering their shells with a pencil.

If it is too dry, the snails sleep in the box. When it threatens to rain, Abel lines them up outside, and if it still doesn't come down, he wakens them by pouring a pot of water over them. And all of them—except the mothers, brooding, he says, in the bottom of the box—stroll out under the care of a dog named Barbare, which is a strip of lead Abel pushes with his thumb.

When I talked to him about the difficulties of their training, I noticed that he shook his head, even when he was answering *yes*.

"Abel," I said, "why are you moving your head that way?"

"It's my sugar," Abel said.

"What sugar?"

"Look, here."

While he is down on all fours, putting number 8 back on the track, I see on Abel's neck, between his skin and his shirt, a lump of sugar hanging on a thread, like a medal.

"Maman puts it on me," he said, "when she wants to punish me."

"Does it bother you?"

"It itches."

"And it stings too, doesn't it! It's all red there."

"But when she forgives me," Abel says, "I eat it."

THE FROGS

With sudden thrusts, they limber up their springs.

They leap out of the grass like heavy drops of frying-oil.

They sit, bronze paper-weights, on the broad waterlily pads.

One crams himself with air. You could put a sou, through his mouth, into the cashbox of his belly.

They rise, like sighs, from the mud.

Motionless, they seem nothing but huge eyes on the surface of the water, the tumors of the smooth pond.

Squatting cross-legged, stupefied, they squint like a tailor and yawn at the setting sun.

Then, like hawkers deafening the streets, they call out the latest news of the day.

There will be a party at their house this evening—can you hear them rinsing their glasses?

Sometimes they snap up a bug.

And others are concerned with nothing but making love.

And all of them tempt the fisherman.

Without much difficulty, I break off a long switch. I have a pin stuck in my overcoat that I bend into a hook.

There's no trouble about the line.

But I still need a wisp of yarn, something red, anything . . . I look through my pockets, on the ground, up in the sky.

I find nothing, and stare mournfully at my buttonhole, ready and waiting, which there has been no hurry embellishing with the red ribbon . . .

Le Crapaud

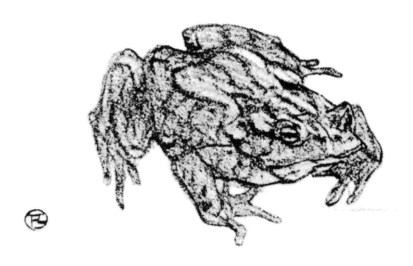

THE TOAD

Born of a stone, he lives under one, and will dig himself a grave there.

I visit him frequently, and each time I lift his stone I'm afraid of finding him, and afraid he won't be there any more.

He's there.

Hidden in this dry lair that is clean, close, all his own, he fills it full, bloated like a miser's purse.

When the rain drives him out, he keeps ahead of me. A few soggy jumps and he comes to rest on his haunches, his reddened eyes staring.

If the world unjustly treats him like a leper, I at least have no fear of crouching close and bringing down to his own my human face.

Then I shall master a vestige of disgust, and caress you, toad!

(There are some one has to swallow in life that taste a lot worse.)

Even so, yesterday I was certainly tactless. He was fermenting and seeping, all his warts had popped.

"My poor friend," I said to him, "I don't want to hurt your feelings, but my God you're ugly!"

He opened his childish toothless mouth, and his breath was warm as he answered with a faint British accent:

"You aren't?"

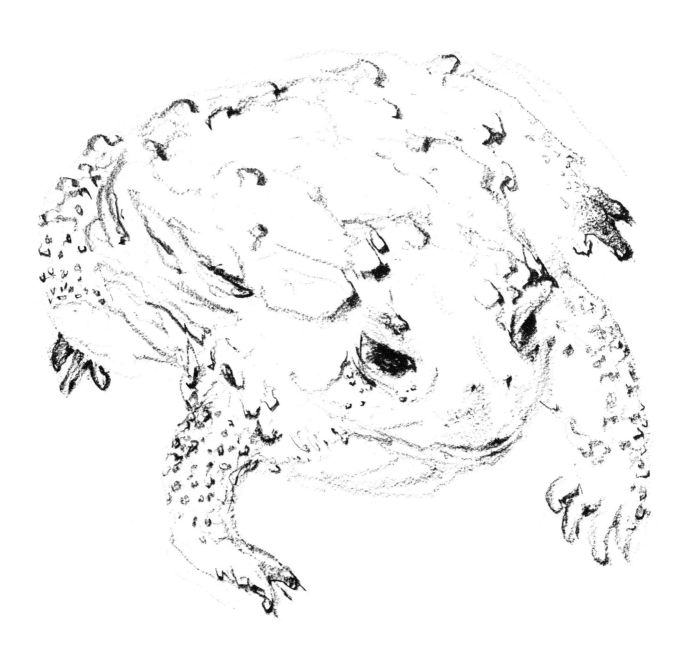

L'Araignée

THE SPIDER

A hairy little black fist, clutching some hair.

All night long, in the moon's name, she affixes her seals.

THE COCKROACH

Black and pasted there like a keyhole.

THE CATERPILLAR

She comes out of a tuft of grass that had hidden her during the hot weather. She crosses the gravel path with tremendous undulations. She is careful not to stop for a minute, and once she thought she was lost in the gardener's footprint.

Having reached the strawberries, she takes a rest, raises her nose to the right and the left to sniff around; then she sets off again and under the leaves, over the leaves, she knows, now, where she is going.

What a lovely caterpillar, fat, hairy, furry, brown with gold specks and those black eyes!

Guided by her sense of smell, she fidgets and puckers like a thick eyebrow.

She stops at the bottom of a rose-tree.

With her delicate clasps, she tests the rough bark, sways her little dog-face and makes up her mind to try the ascent.

And this time, you'd say that she's painfully swallowing each length of the way by deglutition.

At the very top of the rose-tree is blooming a rose the color of an innocent girl. The perfumes she lavishes upon the air intoxicate her—she no longer cares about anything, but lets the first caterpillar to come along climb up her stem. She receives the visitor like a gift.

And anticipating that it will be chilly tonight, she is glad to put a fur boa around her neck.

THE BUTTERFLY

This love-letter folded in two is looking for a flower's address.

THE WASP

You know, she'll end up by ruining her waist!

THE DRAGONFLY

She's treating her ophthalmia.

From one riverbank to the other, she keeps dipping her swollen eyes in the cool water.

And she buzzes, as if she flew by electricity.

THE CRICKET

This is the hour when, tired of wandering, the black insect returns from his promenade and carefully repairs the disorder of his domain.

First of all, he rakes his narrow sandy walks.

He makes some sawdust, which he then spreads on the doorstep of his retreat.

He files down the root of that big weed likely to bother him later on.

He rests.

Then he rewinds his tiny watch.

Is he through? Is it broken? He rests some more.

He goes inside and shuts his door.

For a long time, he turns his key in the delicate lock.

And he listens.

Nothing outside is moving.

But he doesn't feel safe.

And as though by a fine cable whose pulley creaks, he descends into the bowels of the earth.

There is not another sound.

In the silent fields, the poplars rise into the air like fingers, pointing at the moon.

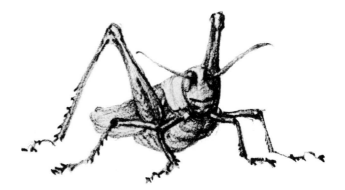

THE GRASSHOPPER

Perhaps he is the insect policeman?

All day he leaps about, hard on the heels of invisible poachers he never catches up with.

The highest weeds fail to stop him.

Nothing frightens him, for he has seven-league boots, a bull-neck, the forehead of a genius, a streamlined belly, celluloid wings, Satanic horns and a huge saber on his behind.

Since one cannot have the virtues of a policeman without the vices, it has to be admitted: the grasshopper is a faker.

If you don't believe me, chase one, catch him on an alfalfa leaf between two leaps, and look carefully at his mouth while you hold him in your hand: through his terrible mandibles he secretes a black froth that looks like tobacco juice.

But already you can't hold him any longer. His hopping rage comes over him again. The green monster escapes with a sudden effort and, fragile, easily dismantled, leaves a tiny thigh in your hand.

THE ANTS

Each one of them looks like the figure 3.
    And there are so many—so many of them!
    There are 33333333333 . . . to infinity.

THE ANT AND THE PARTRIDGE

An ant fell into a rain-filled wagon rut and was about to drown, when a partridge, taking a drink, plucked it out with one tweak of its beak, thereby saving its life.

"I'll make it up to you," the ant promised.

"The days of La Fontaine," replied the skeptical partridge, "are long since past. Not that I question your gratitude, but how in the world could you manage to nip the heel, for instance, of a hunter about to shoot me? Hunters, nowadays, never walk barefoot."

The ant wasted no effort on arguing the point, and made haste to rejoin her sisters, all following the same path, like black beads sliding down a thread.

Now as it happened, the hunter was not far off.

He was taking his ease, lying at full length in the shadow of a tree. Noticing the partridge poking and pecking through the stubble, he stood up and was about to fire, but suddenly realized, from the most unmistakeable evidence, that he had ants in his pants; he was unable to pull the trigger, his hands being required elsewhere, nor did the partridge wait for him to be disengaged.

THE FLEA

A grain of tobacco on springs.

THE SQUIRREL

It's all very well to talk about flourish and *panache*, but my little friend, you don't put it *there*.

MONKEYS . . .

Go see the monkeys (wretched scamps, they've gone and torn all their trousers!) climb, dance in the new sun, quarrel, scratch, peel things, and drink with a primitive grace, while from their eyes, troubled sometimes but not for long, escape certain momentary sparks.

Go see the flamingoes that walk on tongs for fear of wetting their pink petticoats in the pond; the swans and the conceited plumbing of their necks; the ostrich with his baby-chick wings and his stationmaster's cap; the storks that are constantly shrugging their shoulders (after a while, it stops meaning anything); the chilly marabou in its wretched little jacket, and the penguins in their inverness capes; the pelican holding his bill like a wooden saber; and the parakeets, the tamest of which are less thoroughly domesticated than their keeper himself, who ends up taking a ten-sou piece from us, right in his hand!

Go see the yak, burdened with prehistoric thoughts; the giraffe that shows us, over the bars of his cage, his head on the end of a pike; the elephant scuffing his slippers in front of his door, stoop-shouldered, nose down: he almost vanishes in the sack of a pair of trousers pulled up too high, and behind him, a little piece of string hangs out.

And go see the porcupine covered with penholders quite awkward for himself and his lady-friend; the zebra, a transparency model for all the other zebras; the bear that amuses us so much and himself so little; and the lion who yawns until we do too.

Le Cerf

THE BUCK

I entered the woods at one end of the clearing, as he arrived at the other.

At first I thought that someone I didn't know was walking toward me, with a plant on his head.

Then I made out the tiny dwarf tree, with its spread, leafless branches.

Finally the buck appeared clearly, and we both stopped. I spoke first:

"Come on. Don't be afraid. If I have a gun, it's for looks, to imitate the men who take themselves seriously. I never use it, and I leave its cartridges in their drawer."

The buck listened and sniffed my words. As soon as I stopped talking, he didn't hesitate a minute: his legs stirred like stems that a breath of air crosses and uncrosses. He fled.

"What a pity!" I shouted after him. "I was already hoping we could cover some of the road together. I was offering you, in my hand, the kinds of grass you like, and you, at a strolling gait, you were carrying my gun lying in your antlers . . ."

THE GUDGEON

He swims upstream, following the path the pebbles make, for he doesn't like the mud, or the weeds either.

He notices a bottle lying on a bed of sand. There is nothing in it but water. I purposely forgot to put any bait inside. The gudgeon swims around it, looking for the entrance: now he's caught.

I pull up the bottle and dump out the gudgeon.

Farther upstream, he hears a noise. Far from avoiding it, he swims closer, out of curiosity. It's me again, wading in the water and stirring up the bottom with a pole, beside a net. The stubborn gudgeon tries to get through the mesh. He sticks fast.

I pull up the net and dump out the gudgeon.

Downstream, a sudden shock tugs at my line and the two-tone float dips under the surface.

I pull it in: it's the gudgeon again.

I unhook him and toss him back.

This time, I won't have him again.

He's there, motionless, at my feet, under the clear water. I can see his wide head, his big stupid eye, and his barbels.

He yawns, his lip torn, and breathes hard, after such excitement.

But he is incorrigible.

I drop my line again, with the same worm on it.

And right away the gudgeon swallows it.

Which of us will get tired of this first?

They certainly aren't biting tonight. Don't they know the season opened today?

THE WHALE

She has more than enough, right there in her mouth, to make
a corset with—but with a waist like that . . . !

IN THE GARDEN

The Spade: *Fac et spera.*
  The Pick: Me too.

  The Flowers: Will there be sunshine today?
  The Sunflower: Yes, if I say so.
  The Watering-can: Sorry, but if I say so, it will rain, and
if I take off my nozzle, in torrents.

  The Rose-Tree: Oh! What a wind!
  The Stake: I am here.

  The Raspberry: Why do the roses have thorns? You can't
eat a rose.
  The Carp in the pond: Right! That's why I have spines,
because they eat me, and I prick them with mine.
  The Thistle: Yes, but too late.

  The Rose: Do you think I am beautiful?
  The Hornet: I'd have to look at what's underneath.
  The Rose: Come in.

The Bee: Keep it up! Everyone tells me I'm doing such a good job. I hope to be made section chief by the end of the month.

The Violets: We're all club officers.
The White Violets: All the more reason to be modest, sisters.
The Leek: Exactly. Do you hear me boasting?

The Scallion: It smells terrible around here!
The Garlic: I bet it's that carnation again.

The Asparagus: My little finger tells me everything.

The Potato: I think I've just had my babies.

The Apple Tree (To The Pear Tree Opposite): It's your pear, your pear, your pear . . . , it's your pear I want to grow.

THE POPPIES

They explode in the meadow, like an army of little soldiers; but though their red is much finer, they are harmless.

Their sword is a spathe of blossoms.

It is the wind that makes them run, and each poppy lingers, when it wants to, at the edge of the furrow, with the cornflower, its countryman.

THE VINE

All its stocks, props straight, are at Shoulder Arms.

What are they waiting for? The grapes won't come out again this year, and vine-leaves aren't used for anything but statues any more.

THE KINGFISHER

They weren't biting, this evening, but I came home with a rare emotion.

While I was sitting there, holding out my line, a kingfisher came and perched on the rod.

We have no bird more brilliant.

He looked like a big blue flower on the end of a long stem. The rod bent under his weight. I held my breath, proud of being taken for a tree by a kingfisher.

And I'm sure he didn't fly away because he was frightened, but because he thought he was merely passing from one branch to another.

THE NEST OF FINCHES

In a fork of our cherry-tree, there was a pretty nest—round, perfect, all horsehair outside, all down within; and four nestlings had just hatched in it. I said to my father:

"I wish I could have them to raise for myself."

My father had often explained to me that it was a crime to put birds in a cage. But this time, doubtless tired of repeating the same thing, he found nothing to answer. A few days later, I said to him:

"It would be easy—first I'd put the nest in a cage, then I'd fasten the cage in the tree, and the mother-bird would feed the babies through the bars until they wouldn't need her any more."

My father did not tell me what he thought of this plan.

Which is why I installed the nest in a cage, the cage in the cherry-tree, and what I had anticipated duly occurred: the adult finches, without hesitation, brought their young beakful after beakful of caterpillars. And my father watched from a distance, as amused as I was by their bright comings-and-goings, their flight tinged with blood-red and sulfur-yellow.

One evening I said:

"The little birds are full-fledged now. If they were free, they'd fly away. I'll let them spend a last night *en famille,* and tomorrow I'll bring them inside, hang them up in my window, and believe me, they'll be better taken care of than any other finches in the world."

My father offered no argument.

The next day I found the cage empty. There was my father, witnessing my stupefaction.

"I'm not accusing anyone," I said, "but I'd like to know what idiot opened the cage door!"

THE CAGE WITHOUT BIRDS

Felix does not understand how people can keep birds in cages.

"It's a crime," he says, "like picking flowers. Personally, I'd rather sniff them on their stems—and birds are meant to fly, the same way."

Nonetheless he buys a cage, hangs it in his window. He puts a cotton-wool nest inside, a saucer of seeds, and a cup of clean, renewable water. He also hangs a swing in the cage, and a little mirror.

And when he is questioned with some surprise:

"I pride myself on my generosity," he says, "each time I look at that cage. I could put a bird in there, but I leave it empty. If I wanted to, some brown thrush, some fat bullfinch hopping around outside, or some other bird of all the kinds we have here would be a captive. But thanks to me, at least one of them remains free. There's always that . . ."

THE WAGTAIL

She runs as much as she flies, and always right under our feet—
insolent, uncatchable, she challenges us, with her little cries,
to step on her tail.

THE ORIOLE

I say:
  "Give me back that cherry, right now."
  "Fine," the oriole answers. He gives back the cherry and,
with it, the three hundred thousand cutworm larvae that he
swallows in a year.

THE THRUSH

Whatever possessed me to buy a bird?

The man in the shop told me: "This one's a male. Wait a week or so, until he gets used to his new home, and he'll sing all the time."

You know, that bird never makes a sound, and he does everything backward.

As soon as I put seeds in his dish he worries them with his beak until they're scattered all over the cage.

I tie a cracker between two bars. He eats the thread. Then he hammers away at the cracker until it falls down, outside the cage.

He takes baths in his drinking water and drinks out of the bathtub. And leaves his turds in both, all the time.

He thinks a piece of toast is a ready-made thrush-nest and keeps huddling in it.

He hasn't figured out what the lettuce-leaf is for, but he does a good job of shredding it to pieces.

When he really wants to swallow one of his seeds, he's pathetic. He rolls it from one corner of the cage to the other with his beak, squeezes it, breaks it, and twists his head around like an old man who's lost all his teeth.

His lump of sugar is never used. Is it a stone sticking through the bars, a balcony, or an impractical table?

He prefers his wooden perches. He has two, one over the other, criss-crossed, and it's really disgusting to watch him jump back and forth. Like the mechanical stupidity of a clock that can't tell time. What fun can he have, jumping like that, or for what strange necessity does he keep on?

If he takes a rest from his dreary gymnastics, clutching a perch with one foot, the other mechanically gropes for the same perch.

As soon as the winter comes and we light the stove, he thinks it's spring, moulting-time, and sheds his feathers.

The lamplight troubles his nights, mixes up his schedule. He goes to sleep at twilight. I let the shadows deepen around him. Perhaps he's dreaming? I quickly bring the lamp over to the cage, he opens his eyes. Daylight already? And he starts bustling about, dancing, riddling holes in a leaf, spreading his tail, unpasting his wings.

But I blow out the lamp and regret not seeing his startled expression.

Pretty soon I've had enough of this mute creature that can live backward, and I let him go, outside the window . . . He doesn't know what to do with his freedom any more than with his cage. You can catch him in your hand.

Don't bring him back here.

Not only am I not offering any reward—I swear I don't know that bird.

SWALLOWS

They give me my daily lesson.

They stipple the air with tiny shrieks.

They draw a straight line, set a comma at the end, and all of a sudden return to the margin.

They put the house I live in between wild parentheses.

Too quick for the garden pond to make a copy of their flight, they mount from cellar to attic.

With a light wingfeather, they loop inimitable paraphs.

Then, by twos, bracketed, they meet, mingle, and against the blue sky spatter ink.

But only a friendly eye can follow them, and though you know Greek and Latin, I can read the Hebrew the chimney swallows inscribe on the air.

The Finch: If you ask me, the swallow's a fool: imagine thinking a chimney is a tree.

The Bat: Say what you like, of the two of us the swallow flies more clumsily: in broad daylight he's always going the wrong way. If he flew at night, the way I do, he'd be killing himself every minute.

BATS

It's been worn so much the night is getting threadbare.

Not up at the top, where the stars are. It's frayed like a dress that trails along the ground, between stones and trees, all the way to the bottom of smelly tunnels and damp caves.

Pieces of it manage to get in everywhere. And thorns snag it, frosts crack it, mud spoils it. And every morning, when the night climbs back, a few rags come loose, clinging here and there.

That is how bats are born.

And it is because of this origin of theirs that they cannot stand the light of day.

Once the sun sets and we begin feeling chilly, they come loose from the old rafters where they were lethargically hanging by one talon.

Their clumsy flight alarms us. On featherless, whaleboned wings they flutter around us. They find their way—not with their useless wounded eyes, but by ear.

My friend hides her face, and I turn away my head, fearing the tainted impact.

They say that even more ardently than we make love, they would suck our blood until we died.

People exaggerate so!

Bats aren't mean. They never touch us.

Daughters of the night, they hate only lights, and with a rustle of their tiny funereal shawls they hunt for candles to snuff out.

THE MAGPIE

He always has a little snow on him, left over from the last winter.

He hops, feet together, along the ground, and then, flying quite straight, mechanically, he heads for a tree.

Sometimes he misses and can only stop on the next tree.

Commonplace, so despised he seems immortal, dressing up in the morning so he can chatter until night, unbearable in his tails, he is the most French of all our birds.

The Magpie: CACACACACACA.
The Frog: What's he saying?
The Magpie: I'm not saying anything, I'm singing.
The Frog: Kouax!
The Mole: Keep quiet up there, we can't hear ourselves
work!

THE LANGUAGE OF TREES

In my garden there is an old, half-dead willow that frightens the little birds. Only one black bird inhabits its last leaves.

But the rest of the garden is full of young flowering trees in which the bright birds nest, trees that are as lively and bright themselves.

And it seems as though these young trees are mocking the old willow. Every other minute they fling at it, like taunting words, a flight of chattering birds.

One after the other, sparrows, starlings, titmice and finches plague the willow. Their wings nip the tops of its branches. The air crackles with their shrill cries; then they make their escape, and it is another importunate gang which takes off from the young trees.

And as loud as it can, the new horde flouts, cheeps, whistles and screeches.

So from dawn to twilight, like jeering words, finches, titmice, starlings and sparrows are launched from the young trees toward the old willow.

Which sometimes loses patience, stirs its last leaves and produces its black bird, answering with the one French word it knows, the one word that sounds right:

Merle!

The Jay: "Why do you always wear black?"
The Blackbird: "Officer, it's the only thing I have to put on."

THE LARK

I've never seen a lark, and it's no use getting up with the dawn. The lark is not a bird of the earth.

Since this morning, I've been tramping along the furrows, brushing through the dry grass.

Flocks of gray sparrows or goldfinches painted on the wing flutter over the thorn hedges.

The jay passes the trees' reviewing stand in official uniform.

A quail skims the alfalfa and with a chalk-line draws the trajectory of his flight.

Behind the shepherd who knits better than any woman, the sheep follow each other, looking just alike.

And everything is steeped in a light so new that even the raven, which bodes no good, makes me smile.

But listen, the way I listen.

Don't you hear somewhere–up there–pieces of crystal falling into a golden cup?

Who can tell me where the lark sings?

If I look up into the air, the sun burns my eyes.

I have to give up trying to see it.

The lark lives in the sky, and it is the only bird of the sky whose song reaches us.

L'Epervier

THE SPARROW-HAWK

First he describes circles over the village.

He was only a fly, a speck of soot.

He grows larger as his flight narrows.

Sometimes he remains motionless. The barnyard fowl show signs of anxiety. The pigeons return to the roof. A hen, with a brief cry, recalls her chicks, and you can hear the vigilant geese gabbling from one side of the barn to the other.

The sparrow-hawk hesitates and soars at the same height. Perhaps all he wants is the cock on the weathervane.

You'd think he was hung up there in the sky by a thread.

Suddenly the thread breaks, the sparrow-hawk falls, his victim chosen. It is the moment of a drama, here on earth.

But to everyone's astonishment, he stops before he touches the ground, as though he lacks weight altogether, and with a stroke of his wings, he gains altitude again.

He has seen that I am watching him from my door, and that I am hiding, behind me, something long that gleams.

THE CROW

Wha? Wha? Wha?
Not a word.

THE PARTRIDGES

The partridge and the farmer live in peace, he behind his plow, she in the nearby alfalfa, at the right distance from each other not to be inconvenienced. The partridge knows the farmer's voice, she is not afraid of him when he shouts or swears.

When the plow creaks, or the ox coughs, or if the donkey begins braying, she knows it's nothing.

And this peace lasts until I come and trouble it.

But I arrive, and the partridge flies away, the farmer is not at ease, neither is the ox, or the donkey. I fire, and at the uproar of an intruder, all nature is thrown into confusion.

I flush these partridges from the stubble first, then I find them in the alfalfa, then in a pasture, then along a hedge, then in the corner of the woods, then . . .

And all of a sudden I stop, in a sweat, and exclaim:

"Those damn birds are making me run!"

From a distance, I noticed something at the foot of a tree, in the middle of the pasture.

I approach the hedge and look over it.

It seems to me that a bird's neck is sticking up in the shadows. Immediately my heart beats faster. There can only be partridges in those weeds. By a familiar signal, the mother, hearing me, has told them to lie low. She herself is huddling down, and only her neck remains straight up, as she keeps

watch. But I hesitate, for the neck doesn't stir, and I am afraid of being mistaken, of shooting at a root.

Here and there, around the tree, yellow patches, partridges or lumps of dirt manage to confuse my vision completely.

If I flush the birds, the branches of the tree will keep me from firing at them in flight, and I prefer, by shooting at them on the ground, to commit what serious hunters call a murder.

But what I take for a partridge neck still doesn't move.

For a long time I watch it.

If it is a partridge, her immobility and vigilance are remarkable, and all the others, by their way of obeying her, deserve this guardian. Not one moves.

I make a feint: I hide behind the hedge and stop watching, for as long as I see the partridge, she sees me.

Now we're all invisible, in a deathly silence.

Then, once again, I look.

Oh! this time, I'm certain. The partridge thinks I'm gone. The neck has risen, and the movement she makes to pull it in gives her away.

Slowly I bring my rifle butt to my shoulder . . .

In the evening, exhausted and full, before falling into my gamey slumbers, I think of the partridges I've been hunting all day, and I imagine the night they are spending.

They are beside themselves.

Why does one of them not come when the call goes out?

Why are some of them hurt, pecking at their wounds and unable to keep still?

And why have they all been so terrified?

No sooner do they come to rest, now, than the sentinel

sounds the alarm. They must leave again, leave the weeds or the stubble.

All they do is run away, and they are even frightened of the noises they were used to.

They no longer frisk about, or eat, or even sleep.

They don't understand anything.

If the feather that falls from a wounded partridge happens to catch in my proud hunter's hat, I wouldn't find that at all out of the way.

As soon as it rains too much, or is too dry, or my dog loses the scent, or I shoot badly and the partridges become unapproachable, I regard myself in a state of legitimate self-defence.

There are birds—the magpie, the jay, the blackbird, the thrush—against which a self-respecting hunter does not measure himself, and I respect myself.

I only like a fight with the partridges.

They're so cunning!

One of their tricks is to start from far away, but you catch up with them and teach them something about that.

Another is to wait until the hunter has gone past, but behind him they fly up too soon, and he turns around.

Another is to hide in the deep alfalfa, but he heads right for it.

Another is to turn sharply in flight, but that way they come closer together.

Another is to run instead of flying, and they run faster than a man, but there is the dog.

Another is to call to one another when they scatter, but they also call the hunter, and nothing is sweeter to him than their song.

Already this pair of young ones was beginning to live apart. I surprise them, in the evening, on the edge of a plowed field. They fly up so closely joined, wings interlaced almost, that the shot that killed one wounded the other.

One saw nothing and felt nothing, but the other had the time to see his mate dead and to feel himself dying beside her.

Both of them, on the same spot of land, have left a little love, a little blood, and some feathers.

Hunter, with one shot you have killed two splendid birds —go brag about it to your family.

These two old birds from last year whose brood had been destroyed loved each other no less than the young ones. I saw them together all the time. They were clever at avoiding me and I didn't make any effort to pursue them. It was by chance that I killed one of them. And then I hunted down the other, to kill it, too—out of pity!

This one has a broken leg, hanging, as if I were holding it by a thread.

At first that one follows the others until its wings betray it; it collapses, and flutters a little; it runs as long as it can, in front of the dog, light, almost above the furrows.

This one has received a pellet in the head. It separates from the others. It points up into the air, stunned, mounts higher than the trees, higher than a steeple, toward the sun. And the hunter, agonized, loses sight of it when finally it sur-renders to the weight of its heavy head. It closes its wings and dives, beak first, toward the ground, like an arrow.

That one falls, without a sound, like a rag you throw onto the dog's nose to train it.

That one, when the gun goes off, wavers like a tiny boat and capsizes.

You couldn't tell why this one died, so secret is the wound under the feathers.

I stuff this one into my pocket quickly, as if I was afraid of being seen, of seeing myself.

But this one, that doesn't want to die, I have to strangle. Between my fingers, she claws the air, opens her beak, her tiny tongue palpitates, and over her eyes, Homer says, descends the shadow of death.

Over there, the farmer raises his head at my shot and stares at me.

He is a judge, that working man; he's going to speak to me, make me ashamed, with his deep voice.

No: sometimes it's a jealous farmer who's sulky not to be hunting like me, sometimes a good-humored peasant whom I amuse and who tells me where my partridges have gone.

It is never the outraged spokesman of nature herself.

I come home this morning, after five hours walking, game-bag empty, head low and rifle heavy. It is hot enough to be working up to a storm, and my dog, exhausted, walks slowly in front of me, follows the hedges, and often sits down in the shade of a tree and waits for me to catch up.

Suddenly, as I am crossing a field of alfalfa, he falls or rather he flattens himself into a point, a vegetable immobility.

Only the hairs in the tip of his tail quiver. There are, I would swear it, some partridges under his nose. They are there, squeezed together, sheltered from the wind and the sun. They see the dog, they see me, they may even recognize me, and terrified, they don't move.

Wakened from my torpor, I'm ready and I wait. My dog and I won't be the first to move.

Suddenly and simultaneously, the partridges start up: still glued together, they move as one bird, and I shoot into the flock as though my bullet were a blow of my fist. One of them, stunned, pirouettes. The dog leaps on it and brings me back a bloody rag, half a partridge. The blow of the fist has taken off the rest.

All right, at least we're not empty-handed! The dog frolics ahead, and I swagger a little myself.

What I deserve is a good round of birdshot in the behind!

THE WOODCOCK

All that was left of an April sun were the pink gleams in the clouds which had stopped moving, as though they had arrived.

The night was rising from the ground and gradually enrobing us, in the little clearing where my father was waiting for the woodcocks.

Standing beside him, I couldn't see anything clearly except his face. Taller than I, he couldn't see me at all, and the dog was panting, invisible, at our feet.

The thrushes were hurrying back into the woods and the blackbird uttered his guttural cry, that kind of whinny which is an order to all birds to be still and go to sleap.

Soon the woodcock would leave his lair of dead leaves and get up. When it is mild, like that evening, he lingers before reaching the field. He hops around the woods, looking for a companion. From his faint call, you can tell whether he is coming closer or not. Then he flies heavily between the big oaks, and his long beak hangs so low that he seems to be strolling through the air with a little cane.

While I was peering in all directions, listening hard, my father suddenly fired, but did not follow the dog that dashed ahead.

"Did you miss him?" I asked.

"I didn't shoot," he said. "My gun just went off in my hands."

"All by itself?"

"Yes."

"Oh . . . Could it have been a branch?"

"I don't know."

I heard him taking out the empty cartridge.

"How were you holding it?"

Hadn't he understood?

"I'm asking you which way the gun was pointing?"

Since he didn't answer, I didn't dare speak another word. Finally, I said:

"You might have killed . . . the dog."

"Let's go home," my father said.

END OF THE HUNTING SEASON

It's a poor day, gray and brief, as though gnawed off at both ends.

Around noon, the sulky sun tries to pierce the mist and half-opens a pale eye that is immediately shut again.

I walk where my steps take me. My gun is no use, and the dog, usually so wild, keeps at my heels.

The river water is disturbingly transparent: if you stuck your fingers in it, the water would cut them like broken glass.

In the stubble, at each of my steps a stupefied lark whirrs up. They gather, swirl, and their flight scarcely troubles the frozen air.

Over there, congregations of crows peck away, disinterring the autumn sowing.

Three partridges stand up in the middle of a field whose stubble no longer shelters them.

How they've grown! They're real ladies now. They listen, anxious: I saw them all right, but I leave them in peace and walk on. And somewhere, no doubt, a hare that was trembling is reassured and puts his nose back on the edge of his burrow.

All along this hedge (here and there a last leaf flutters its wing like a bird with one leg caught), a blackbird makes his getaway as I approach, hiding farther on, then shoots out under the dog's nose and, running no risk, mocks us both.

Gradually the mist thickens. I might be lost. My gun is no more than a stick that might go off in my hands. What is the source of that vague sound, that lowing, that clanging, that human cry?

I must get back. By a path already faint, I return to the village, which alone knows its name. A few farmers live here, and no one ever comes to see them, except me.

A FAMILY OF TREES

It was after having crossed a sun-baked field that I met up with them. They don't live on the edge of the road, because of the noise. They inhabit fallow fields, near a spring known only to the birds.

From a distance, they seem impenetrable. As soon as I approach, their trunks move apart. They greet me diffidently. I can rest, refresh myself, but I can tell they are watching me, a little suspiciously.

They live *en famille,* the oldest in the middle and the little ones, the ones whose first leaves have just been born, just about everywhere, without ever moving very far away.

They take a long time to die, and they keep their dead standing until they fall into dust.

They caress each other with their long branches, to make sure they are all there, like the blind. The gesticulate angrily if the wind wears itself out trying to uproot them. But they never quarrel among themselves. They murmur only in agreement.

I feel that they should be my true family. I'd soon forget the other one. These trees will adopt me little by little, and to deserve it, I learn what I must know:

Already I know how to watch the clouds passing.

And I know how to stay in one place.

And I almost know how to keep still.

239

JULES RENARD
HISTOIRES NATURELLES

le chasseur d'images

* **34**

Il saute du lit de bon matin, et ne part que si son esprit est net, son cœur pur, son corps léger comme un vêtement d'été. Il n'emporte point de provisions. Il boira l'air frais en route et reniflera les odeurs salubres. Il laisse ses armes à la maison et se contente d'ouvrir les yeux. Les yeux servent de filets où les images s'emprisonnent d'elles-mêmes.

La première qu'il fait captive est celle du chemin qui montre ses os, cailloux polis, et ses ornières, veines crevées, entre deux haies riches de prunelles et de mûres.

Il prend ensuite l'image de la rivière. Elle blanchit aux coudes et dort sous la caresse des saules. Elle miroite quand un poisson tourne le ventre, comme si on jetait une pièce d'argent, et, dès que tombe une pluie fine, la rivière a la chair de poule.

Il lève l'image des blés mobiles, des luzernes appétissantes et des prairies ourlées de ruisseaux. Il saisit au passage le vol d'une alouette ou d'un chardonneret.

Puis il entre au bois. Il ne se savait pas doué de sens si délicats. Vite imprégné de parfums, il ne perd aucune sourde rumeur, et, pour qu'il communique avec les arbres, ses nerfs se lient aux nervures des feuilles.

Bientôt, vibrant jusqu'au malaise, il perçoit trop, il fermente, il a peur, quitte le bois et suit de loin les paysans mouleurs regagnant le village.

Dehors, il fixe un moment, au point que son œil éclate, le soleil qui se couche et dévêt sur l'horizon ses lumineux habits, ses nuages répandus pêle-mêle.

Enfin, rentré chez lui, la tête pleine, il éteint sa lampe et longuement, avant de s'endormir, il se plaît à compter ses images.

Dociles, elles renaissent au gré du souvenir. Chacune d'elles en éveille une autre, et sans cesse leur troupe phosphorescente s'accroît de nouvelles venues, comme des perdrix poursuivies et divisées tout le jour chantent le soir, à l'abri du danger, et se rappellent au creux des sillons.

la poule

36

Pattes jointes, elle saute du poulailler, dès qu'on lui ouvre la porte.

C'est une poule commune, modestement parée et qui ne pond jamais d'œufs d'or.

Éblouie de lumière, elle fait quelques pas, indécise, dans la cour.

Elle voit d'abord le tas de cendres où, chaque matin, elle a coutume de s'ébattre.

Elle s'y roule, s'y trempe, et, d'une vive agitation d'ailes, les plumes gonflées, elle secoue ses puces de la nuit.

Puis elle va boire au plat creux que la dernière averse a rempli.

Elle ne boit que de l'eau.

Elle boit par petits coups et dresse le col, en équilibre sur le bord du plat.

Ensuite elle cherche sa nourriture éparse.

Les fines herbes sont à elles, et les insectes et les graines perdues.

Elle pique, elle pique, infatigable.

De temps en temps, elle s'arrête.

Droite sous son bonnet phrygien, l'œil vif, le jabot avantageux, elle écoute de l'une et de l'autre oreille.

Et, sûre qu'il n'y a rien de neuf, elle se remet en quête.

Elle lève haut ses pattes raides, comme ceux qui ont la goutte. Elle écarte les doigts et les pose avec précaution, sans bruit.

On dirait qu'elle marche pieds nus.

coqs

39

I

Il n'a jamais chanté. Il n'a pas couché une nuit dans un poulailler, connu une seule poule.

Il est en bois, avec une patte de fer au milieu du ventre, et il vit, depuis des années et des années, sur une vieille église comme on n'ose plus en bâtir. Elle ressemble à une grange et le faîte de ses tuiles s'aligne aussi droit que le dos d'un bœuf.

Or, voici que des maçons paraissent à l'autre bout de l'église.

Le coq de bois les regarde, quand un brusque coup de vent le force à tourner le dos.

Et, chaque fois qu'il se retourne, de nouvelles pierres lui bouchent un peu plus de son horizon.

Bientôt, d'une saccade levant la tête, il aperçoit, à la pointe du clocher qu'on vient de finir, un jeune coq qui n'était pas là ce matin. Cet étranger porte haut sa queue, ouvre le bec comme ceux qui chantent, et l'aile sur la hanche, tout battant neuf, il éclate en plein soleil.

D'abord les deux coqs luttent de mobilité. Mais le vieux coq de bois s'épuise vite et se rend. Sous son unique pied, la poutre menace ruine. Il penche, raidi, près de tomber. Il grince et s'arrête.

Et voilà les charpentiers.

Ils abattent ce coin vermoulu de l'église, descendent le coq et le promènent par le village. Chacun peut le toucher, moyennant cadeau.

Ceux-ci donnent un œuf, ceux-là un sou, et Mme Loriot une pièce d'argent.

Les charpentiers boivent de bons coups, et, après s'être disputé le coq,

ils décident de le brûler.

Lui ayant fait un nid de paille et de fagot, ils y mettent le feu.

Le coq de bois pétille clair et sa flamme monte au ciel qu'il a bien gagné.

II

Chaque matin, au saut du perchoir, le coq regarde si l'autre est toujours là, — et l'autre y est toujours.

Le coq peut se vanter d'avoir battu tous ses rivaux de la terre, — mais l'autre, c'est le rival invincible, hors d'atteinte.

Le coq jette cris sur cris : il appelle, il provoque, il menace, — mais l'autre ne répond qu'à ses heures, et d'abord il ne répond pas.

Le coq fait le beau, gonfle ses plumes, qui ne sont pas mal, celles-ci bleues, et celles-là argentées, — mais l'autre, en plein azur, est éblouissant d'or.

Le coq rassemble ses poules, et marche à leur tête. Voyez : elles sont à lui; toutes l'aiment et toutes le craignent, — mais l'autre est adoré des hirondelles.

Le coq se prodigue : il pose, çà et là, ses virgules d'amour, et triomphe, d'un ton aigu, de petits riens; — mais justement l'autre se marie et carillonne à toute volée ses noces de village.

Le coq jaloux monte sur ses ergots pour un combat suprême; sa queue a l'air d'un pan de manteau que relève une épée. Il défie, le sang à la crête, tous les coqs du ciel, — mais l'autre, qui n'a pas peur de faire face aux vents d'orage, joue en ce moment avec la brise et tourne le dos.

Et le coq s'exaspère jusqu'à la fin du jour.

Ses poules rentrent, une à une. Il reste seul, enroué, vanné, dans la cour déjà sombre, — mais l'autre éclate encore aux derniers feux du soleil, et chante, de sa voix pure, le pacifique angélus du soir.

---

canards

45

C'est la cane qui va la première, boitant des deux pattes, barboter au trou qu'elle connaît.

Le canard la suit. Les pointes de ses ailes croisées sur le dos, il boite aussi des deux pattes.

Et cane et canard marchent taciturnes comme à un rendez-vous d'affaires.

La cane d'abord se laisse glisser dans l'eau boueuse où flottent des plumes, des fientes, une feuille de vigne, et de la paille. Elle a presque disparu.

Elle attend. Elle est prête.

Et le canard entre à son tour. Il noie ses riches couleurs. On ne voit que sa tête verte et l'accroche-cœur du derrière. Tous deux se trouvent bien là. L'eau chauffe. Jamais on ne la vide et elle ne se renouvelle que les jours d'orage.

Le canard, de son bec aplati, mordille et serre la nuque de la cane. Un instant il s'agite et l'eau est si épaisse qu'elle en frissonne à peine. Et vite calmée, plate, elle réfléchit, en noir, un coin de ciel pur.

La cane et le canard ne bougent plus. Le soleil les cuit et les endort. On passerait près d'eux sans les remarquer. Ils ne se dénoncent que par les rares bulles d'air qui viennent crever sur l'eau croupie.

l'oie

48

Tiennette voudrait aller à Paris, comme les autres filles du village. Mais est-elle seulement capable de garder ses oies?

A vrai dire, elle les suit plutôt qu'elle ne les mène. Elle tricote, machinale, derrière leur troupe, et elle s'en rapporte à l'oie de Toulouse qui a la raison d'une grande personne.

L'oie de Toulouse connaît le chemin, les bonnes herbes, et l'heure où il faut rentrer.

Si brave que le jars l'est moins, elle protège ses sœurs contre le mauvais chien. Son col vibre et serpente à ras de terre, puis se redresse, et elle domine Tiennette effarée. Dès que tout va

bien, elle triomphe et chante du nez qu'elle sait grâce à qui l'ordre règne.

Elle ne doute pas qu'elle ferait mieux encore.

Et, un soir, elle quitte le pays.

Elle s'éloigne sur la route, bec au vent, plumes collées. Des femmes, qu'elle croise, n'osent l'arrêter. Elle marche vite à faire peur.

Et pendant que Tiennette, restée là-bas, finit de s'abêtir, et, toute pareille aux oies, ne s'en distingue plus, l'oie de Toulouse vient à Paris.

la dinde

51   **I**

Elle se pavane au milieu de la cour, comme si elle vivait sous l'ancien régime.

Les autres volailles ne font que manger toujours, n'importe quoi. Elle, entre ses repas réguliers, ne se préoccupe que d'avoir bel air. Toutes ses plumes sont empesées et les pointes de ses ailes raient le sol, comme pour tracer la route qu'elle suit : c'est là qu'elle s'avance et non ailleurs.

Elle se rengorge tant qu'elle ne voit jamais ses pattes.

Elle ne doute de personne, et, dès que je m'approche, elle s'imagine que je veux lui rendre mes hommages.

Déjà elle glougloute d'orgueil.

— Noble dinde, lui dis-je, si vous étiez une oie, j'écrirais votre éloge, comme le fit Buffon, avec une de vos plumes. Mais vous n'êtes qu'une dinde.

J'ai dû la vexer, car le sang monte à sa tête. Des grappes de colère lui pendent au bec. Elle a une crise de rouge. Elle fait claquer d'un coup sec l'éventail de sa queue et cette vieille chipie me tourne le dos.

II

Sur la route, voici encore le pensionnat des dindes.

Chaque jour, quelque temps qu'il fasse, elles se promènent.

Elles ne craignent ni la pluie, personne ne se retrousse mieux qu'une dinde, ni le soleil, une dinde ne sort jamais sans son ombrelle.

la pintade

55

C'est la bossue de ma cour. Elle ne rêve que plaies à cause de sa bosse.

Les poules ne lui disent rien : brusquement, elle se précipite et les harcèle.

Puis elle baisse sa tête, penche le corps, et, de toute la vitesse de ses pattes maigres, elle court frapper, de son bec dur, juste au centre de la roue d'une dinde.

Cette poseuse l'agaçait.

Ainsi, la tête bleuie, ses barbillons à vif, cocardière, elle rage du matin au soir. Elle se bat sans motif, peut-être parce qu'elle s'imagine toujours qu'on se moque de sa taille, de son crâne chauve et de sa queue basse.

Et elle ne cesse de jeter un cri discordant qui perce l'air comme une pointe.

Parfois elle quitte la cour et disparaît. Elle laisse aux volailles pacifiques un moment de répit. Mais elle revient plus turbulente et plus criarde. Et, frénétique, elle se vautre par terre.

Qu'a-t-elle donc?

La sournoise fait une farce.

Elle est allée pondre son œuf à la campagne.

Je peux le chercher si ça m'amuse.

Elle se roule dans la poussière, comme une bossue.

les pigeons

61

Qu'ils fassent sur la maison un bruit de tambour voilé;

Qu'ils sortent de l'ombre, culbutent, éclatent au soleil et rentrent dans l'ombre;

Que leur col fugitif vive et meure comme l'opale au doigt;

Qu'ils s'endorment, le soir, dans la forêt, si pressés que la plus haute branche du chêne menace de rompre sous cette charge de fruits peints;

Que ces deux-là échangent des saluts frénétiques et brusquement, l'un à l'autre, se convulsent;

Que celui-ci revienne d'exil, avec une lettre, et vole comme la pensée de notre amie lointaine (Ah! un gage!);

Tous ces pigeons, qui d'abord amusent, finissent par ennuyer.

Ils ne sauraient tenir en place et les voyages ne les forment point.

Ils restent toute la vie un peu niais. Ils s'obstinent à croire qu'on fait les enfants par le bec.

Et c'est insupportable à la longue, cette manie héréditaire d'avoir toujours dans la gorge quelque chose qui ne passe pas.

LES DEUX PIGEONS. — Viens mon grrros,... viens mon grrros... viens mon grrros...

le paon

67

Il va sûrement se marier aujourd'hui.

Ce devait être pour hier. En habit de gala, il était prêt. Il n'attendait que sa fiancée. Elle n'est pas venue. Elle ne peut tarder.

Glorieux, il se promène avec une allure de prince indien et porte sur lui les riches présents d'usage. L'amour avive l'éclat de ses couleurs et son aigrette tremble comme une lyre.

La fiancée n'arrive pas.

Il monte au haut du toit et regarde du côté du soleil. Il jette son cri diabolique :

Léon! Léon!

C'est ainsi qu'il appelle sa fiancée. Il ne voit rien venir et personne ne répond. Les volailles habituées ne lèvent même point la tête. Elles sont lasses de l'admirer. Il redescend dans la cour, si sûr d'être beau qu'il est incapable de rancune.

Son mariage sera pour demain.

Et, ne sachant que faire du reste de la journée, il se dirige vers le perron. Il gravit les marches, comme des marches de temple, d'un pas officiel.

Il relève sa robe à queue toute lourde des yeux qui n'ont pu se détacher d'elle.

Il répète encore une fois la cérémonie.

le cygne

71

Il glisse sur le bassin, comme un traîneau blanc, de nuage en nuage. Car il n'a faim que des nuages floconneux qu'il voit naître, bouger, et se perdre dans l'eau. C'est l'un d'eux qu'il désire. Il le vise du bec, et il plonge tout à coup son col vêtu de neige.

Puis, tel un bras de femme sort d'une manche, il le retire.

Il n'a rien.

Il regarde : les nuages effarouchés ont disparu.

Il ne reste qu'un instant désabusé, car les nuages tardent peu à revenir, et, là-bas, où meurent les ondulations de l'eau, en voici un qui se reforme.

Doucement, sur son léger coussin de plumes, le cygne rame et s'approche...

Il s'épuise à pêcher de vains reflets, et peut-être qu'il mourra, victime de cette illusion, avant d'attraper un seul morceau de nuage.

Mais qu'est-ce que je dis?

Chaque fois qu'il plonge, il fouille du bec la vase nourrissante et ramène un ver.

Il engraisse comme une oie.

le chien

75

On ne peut mettre Pointu dehors, par ce temps, et l'aigre sifflet du vent sous la porte l'oblige même à quitter le paillasson. Il cherche mieux et glisse sa bonne tête entre nos sièges. Mais nous nous penchons, serrés, coude à coude, sur le feu, et je donne une claque à Pointu. Mon père le repousse du pied. Maman lui dit des injures. Ma sœur lui offre un verre vide.

Pointu éternue et va voir à la cuisine si nous y sommes.

Puis il revient, force notre cercle, au risque d'être étranglé par les genoux, et le voilà dans un coin de la cheminée.

Après avoir longtemps tourné sur place, il s'assied près du chenet et ne

bouge plus. Il regarde ses maîtres, d'un œil si doux qu'on le tolère. Seulement le chenet presque rouge et les cendres écartées lui brûlent le derrière.

Il reste tout de même.

On lui ouvre un passage :

— Allons, file! es-tu bête!

Mais il s'obstine. A l'heure où les dents des chiens perdus crissent de froid, Pointu, au chaud, poil roussi, fesses cuites, se retient de hurler et rit jaune, avec des larmes plein les yeux...

le chat

81

Le mien ne mange pas les souris; il n'aime pas ça. Il n'en attrape une que pour jouer avec.

Quand il a bien joué, il lui fait grâce de la vie, et il va rêver ailleurs, l'innocent, assis dans la boucle de sa queue, la tête bien fermée comme un poing.

Mais, à cause des griffes, la souris est morte.

la vache

82

Las de chercher, on a fini par ne pas lui donner de nom.

Elle s'appelle simplement « la vache » et c'est le nom qui lui va le mieux.

D'ailleurs, qu'importe, pourvu qu'elle mange!

Or, l'herbe fraîche, le foin sec, les légumes, le grain et même le pain et le sel, elle a tout à discrétion, et elle mange de tout, tout le temps, deux fois, puisqu'elle rumine.

Dès qu'elle m'a vu, elle accourt d'un petit pas léger, en sabots fendus, la peau bien tirée sur ses pattes comme un bas blanc, elle arrive certaine que j'apporte quelque chose qui se mange. Et l'admirant chaque fois, je ne peux que lui dire : Tiens, mange!

Mais de ce qu'elle absorbe elle fait du lait et non de la graisse. A heure fixe, elle offre son pis plein et carré. Elle ne retient pas le lait, — il y a des vaches qui le retiennent, — généreusement, par ses quatre trayons élastiques, à peine pressés, elle vide sa fontaine. Elle ne remue ni le pied, ni la queue, mais de sa langue énorme et souple, elle s'amuse a lécher le dos de la servante.

Quoiqu'elle vive seule, l'appétit l'empêche de s'ennuyer. Il est rare qu'elle beugle de regret au souvenir vague de son dernier veau. Mais elle aime les visites, accueillante avec ses cornes relevées sur le front, et ses lèvres affriandées d'où pendent un fil d'eau et un brin d'herbe.

Les hommes, qui ne craignent rien, flattent son ventre débordant; les femmes, étonnées qu'une si grosse bête soit si douce, ne se défient plus que de ses caresses et font des rêves de bonheur.

Elle aime que je la gratte entre les cornes. Je recule un peu, parce qu'elle s'approche de plaisir, et la bonne grosse bête se laisse faire, jusqu'à ce que j'aie mis le pied dans sa bouse.

la mort de brunette

87

Philippe, qui me réveille, me dit qu'il s'est levé la nuit pour l'écouter et qu'elle avait le souffle calme.

Mais, depuis ce matin, elle l'inquiète.

Il lui donne du foin sec et elle le laisse.

Il offre un peu d'herbe fraîche, et Brunette, d'ordinaire si friande, y touche à peine. Elle ne regarde plus son veau et supporte mal ses coups de nez quand il se dresse, sur ses pattes rigides, pour téter.

Philippe les sépare et attache le veau loin de la mère. Brunette n'a pas l'air de s'en apercevoir.

L'inquiétude de Philippe nous gagne tous. Les enfants même veulent se lever.

Le vétérinaire arrive, examine Brunette et la fait sortir de l'écurie. Elle se cogne au mur et elle bute contre le pas de la porte. Elle tomberait; il faut la rentrer.

— Elle est bien malade, dit le vétérinaire.

Nous n'osons pas lui demander ce qu'elle a.

Il craint une fièvre de lait, souvent fatale, surtout aux bonnes laitières, et se rappelant, une à une, celles qu'on croyait perdues et qu'il a sauvées, il écarte, avec un pinceau, sur les reins de Brunette, le liquide d'une fiole.

— Il agira comme un vésicatoire, dit-il. J'en ignore la composition exacte. Ça vient de Paris. Si le mal ne gagne pas le cerveau, elle s'en tirera toute seule, sinon j'emploierai la méthode de l'eau glacée. Elle étonne les paysans simples, mais je sais à qui je parle.

— Faites, Monsieur.

Brunette, couchée sur la paille, peut encore supporter le poids de sa tête. Elle cesse de ruminer. Elle semble retenir sa respiration pour mieux entendre ce qui se passe au fond d'elle.

On l'enveloppe d'une couverture de laine, parce que les cornes et les oreilles se refroidissent.

— Jusqu'à ce que les oreilles tombent, dit Philippe, il y a de l'espoir.

Deux fois elle essaie en vain de se mettre sur ses jambes. Elle souffle fort, par intervalles de plus en plus espacés.

Et voilà qu'elle laisse tomber sa tête sur son flanc gauche.

— Ça se gâte, dit Philippe accroupi et murmurant des douceurs.

La tête se relève et se rabat sur le bord de la mangeoire, si pesamment que le choc sourd nous fait faire : oh!

Nous bordons Brunette de tas de paille pour qu'elle ne s'assomme pas.

Elle tend le cou et les pattes, elle s'allonge de toute sa longueur, comme au pré, par les temps orageux.

Le vétérinaire se décide à la saigner. Il ne s'approche pas trop. Il est aussi savant qu'un autre, mais il passe pour moins hardi.

Aux premiers coups du marteau de bois, la lancette glisse sur la veine. Après un coup mieux assuré, le sang jaillit dans le seau d'étain que d'habitude le lait emplit jusqu'au bord.

Pour arreter le jet, le vétérinaire passe dans la veine une épingle d'acier.

Puis, du front à la queue de Brunette soulagée, nous appliquons un drap mouillé d'eau de puits et qu'on renouvelle fréquemment parce qu'il s'échauffe vite. Elle ne frissonne même pas. Philippe la tient ferme par les cornes et empêche la tête d'aller battre le flanc gauche.

Brunette, comme domptée, ne bouge plus. On ne sait pas si elle va mieux ou si son état s'aggrave.

Nous sommes tristes, mais la tristesse de Philippe est morne comme celle d'un animal qui en verrait souffrir un autre.

Sa femme lui apporte sa soupe du matin qu'il mange sans appétit, sur un escabeau, et qu'il n'achève pas.

— C'est la fin, dit-il, Brunette enfle!

Nous doutons d'abord, mais Philippe a dit vrai. Elle gonfle à vue d'œil, et ne se dégonfle pas, comme si l'air entré ne pouvait ressortir.

La femme de Philippe demande :

— Elle est morte?

— Tu ne le vois pas! dit Philippe durement.

Mme Philippe sort dans la cour.

— Ce n'est pas près que j'aille en chercher une autre, dit Philippe.

— Une quoi?

— Une autre Brunette.

— Vous irez quand je voudrai, dis-je d'une voix de maître qui m'étonne.

Nous tâchons de nous faire croire que l'accident nous irrite plus qu'il ne nous peine, et déjà nous disons que Brunette est crevée.

Mais le soir, j'ai rencontré le sonneur de l'église, et je ne sais pas ce qui m'a retenu de lui dire :

— Tiens, voilà cent sous, va sonner le glas de quelqu'un qui est mort dans ma maison.

le bœuf

91

La porte s'ouvre ce matin, comme d'habitude, et Castor quitte, sans buter, l'écurie. Il boit à lentes gorgées sa part au fond de l'auge et laisse la part de Pollux attardé. Puis, le mufle s'égouttant ainsi que l'arbre après l'averse, il va de bonne volonté, avec ordre et pesanteur, se ranger à sa place ordinaire, sous le joug du chariot.

Les cornes liées, la tête immobile, il fronce le ventre, chasse mollement de sa queue les mouches noires et, telle une servante sommeille le balai à la main, il rumine en attendant Pollux.

Mais, par la cour, les domestiques affairés crient et jurent et le chien jappe comme à l'approche d'un étranger.

Est-ce le sage Pollux qui, pour la première fois, résiste à l'aiguillon, tournaille, heurte le flanc de Castor, fume, et quoique attelé, tâche encore de secouer le joug commun?

Non, c'est un autre.

Castor, dépareillé, arrête ses mâchoires, quand il voit, près du sien, cet œil trouble de bœuf qu'il ne reconnaît pas.

Au soleil qui se couche, les bœufs trainent par le pré, à pas lents, la herse légère de leur ombre.

les mouches d'eau

94

Il n'y a qu'un chêne au milieu du pré, et les bœufs occupent toute l'ombre de ses feuilles.

La tête basse, ils font les cornes au soleil.

Ils seraient bien, sans les mouches.

Mais aujourd'hui, vraiment, elles dévorent. Acres et nombreuses, les noires se collent par plaques de suie aux yeux, aux narines, aux coins des lèvres même, et les vertes sucent de préférence la dernière écorchure.

Quand un bœuf remue son tablier de cuir, ou frappe du sabot la terre sèche, le nuage des mouches se déplace avec murmure. On dirait qu'elles fermentent.

Il fait si chaud que les vieilles femmes, sur leur porte, flairent l'orage, et déjà elles plaisantent de peur :

— Gare au bourdoudou! disent-elles.

Là-bas, un premier coup de lance lumineux perce le ciel, sans bruit. Une goutte de pluie tombe.

Les bœufs, avertis, relèvent la tête, se meuvent jusqu'au bord du chêne et soufflent patiemment.

Ils le savent : voici que les bonnes mouches viennent chasser les mauvaises.

D'abord rares, une par une, puis serrées, toutes ensemble, elles fondent, du ciel déchiqueté, sur l'ennemi qui cède peu à peu, s'éclaircit, se disperse.

Bientôt, du nez camus à la queue inusable, les bœufs ruisselants ondulent d'aise sous l'essaim victorieux des mouches d'eau.

le taureau

97

Le pêcheur à la ligne volante marche d'un pas léger au bord de l'Yonne et fait sautiller sur l'eau sa mouche verte.

Les mouches vertes, il les attrape aux troncs des peupliers polis par le frottement du bétail.

Il jette sa ligne d'un coup sec et tire d'autorité.

Il s'imagine que chaque place nouvelle est la meilleure, et bientôt il la quitte, enjambe un échalier et de ce pré passe dans l'autre.

Soudain, comme il traverse un grand pré que grille le soleil, il s'arrête.

Là-bas, du milieu des vaches paisibles et couchées, le taureau vient de se lever pesamment.

C'est un taureau fameux et sa taille étonne les passants sur la route. On l'admire à distance et, s'il ne l'a fait déjà, il pourrait lancer son homme au ciel, ainsi qu'une flèche, avec l'arc de ses cornes. Plus doux qu'un agneau tant qu'il veut, il se met tout à coup en fureur, quand ça le prend et, près de lui, on ne sait jamais ce qui arrivera.

Le pêcheur l'observe obliquement.

— Si je fuis, pense-t-il, le taureau sera sur moi avant que je ne sorte du pré. Si, sans savoir nager, je plonge dans la rivière, je me noie. Si je fais le mort par terre, le taureau, dit-on, me flairera et ne me touchera pas. Est-ce bien sûr? Et, s'il ne s'en va plus, quelle angoisse! Mieux vaut feindre une indifférence trompeuse.

Et le pêcheur a la ligne volante continue de pêcher, comme si le taureau était absent. Il espère ainsi lui donner le change.

Sa nuque cuit sous son chapeau de paille.

Il retient ses pieds qui brûlent de courir et les oblige à fouler l'herbe. Il a l'heroïsme de tremper dans l'eau sa mouche verte. Il ne se cache que de temps en temps, derrière les peupliers. Il gagne posément l'échalier de la haie, d'où il pourra, d'un dernier effort de ses membres rompus, bondir hors du pré, sain et sauf.

D'ailleurs, qui le presse?

Le taureau ne s'occupe pas de lui et reste avec les vaches.

Il ne s'est mis debout que pour remuer, par lassitude, comme on s'étire.

Il tourne au vent du soir sa tête crépue.

Il beugle par intervalles, l'œil à demi fermé.

Il mugit de langueur et s'écoute mugir.

Les femmes le reconnaissent aux poils frisés qu'il a sur le front.

le cheval

101

Il n'est pas beau, mon cheval. Il a trop de nœuds et de salières, les côtes plates, une queue de rat et des incisives d'Anglaise. Mais il m'attendrit. Je n'en reviens pas qu'il reste à mon service et se laisse, sans révolte, tourner et retourner.

Chaque fois que je l'attelle, je m'attends qu'il me dise : *non*, d'un signe brusque, et détale.

Point. Il baisse et lève sa grosse tête comme pour remettre un chapeau d'aplomb, recule avec docilité entre les brancards.

Aussi je ne lui ménage ni l'avoine ni le maïs. Je le brosse jusqu'à ce que le poil brille comme une cerise. Je peigne sa crinière, je tresse sa queue maigre. Je le flatte de la main et de la voix. J'éponge ses yeux, je cire ses pieds.

Est-ce que ça le touche?

On ne sait pas.

Il pète.

C'est surtout quand il me promène en voiture que je l'admire. Je le fouette et il accélère son allure. Je l'arrête et il m'arrête. Je tire la guide à gauche et il oblique à gauche, au lieu d'aller à droite et de me jeter dans le fossé avec des coups de sabots quelque part.

Il me fait peur, il me fait honte et il me fait pitié.

Est-ce qu'il ne va pas bientôt se réveiller de son demi-sommeil, et prenant d'autorité ma place, me réduire à la sienne?

A quoi pense-t-il?

Il pète, pète, pète.

l'âne

105

Tout lui est égal. Chaque matin, il voiture, d'un petit pas sec et dru de fonctionnaire, le facteur Jacquot qui distribue aux villages les commissions faites en ville, les épices, le pain, la viande de boucherie, quelques journaux, une lettre.

Cette tournée finie, Jacquot et l'âne travaillent pour leur compte. La voiture sert de charrette. Ils vont ensemble à la vigne, au bois, aux pommes de terre. Ils ramènent tantôt des légumes, tantôt des balais verts, ça ou autre chose, selon le jour.

Jacquot ne cesse de dire : « Hue! hue! » sans motif, comme il ronflerait. Parfois l'âne, à cause d'un chardon qu'il flaire, ou d'une idée qui le prend, ne marche plus. Jacquot lui met un bras autour du cou et pousse. Si l'âne résiste, Jacquot lui mord l'oreille.

Ils mangent dans les fossés, le maître une croûte et des oignons, la bête ce qu'elle veut.

Ils ne rentrent qu'à la nuit. Leurs ombres passent avec lenteur d'un arbre à l'autre.

Subitement, le lac de silence où les choses baignent et dorment déjà, se rompt, bouleversé.

Quelle ménagère tire, à cette heure, par un treuil rouillé et criard, des pleins seaux d'eau de son puits?

C'est l'âne qui remonte et jette toute sa voix dehors et brait, jusqu'à extinction, qu'il s'en fiche, qu'il s'en fiche.

ANE
Le lapin devenu grand.

le cochon

111

Grognon, mais familier comme si nous t'avions gardé ensemble, tu fourres le nez partout et tu marches autant avec lui qu'avec les pattes.

Tu caches sous des oreilles en feuilles de betterave tes petits yeux cassis.

Tu es ventru comme une groseille à maquereau.

Tu as de longs poils comme elle, comme elle la peau claire et une courte queue bouclée.

Et les méchants t'appellent : « Sale cochon! »

Ils disent que, si rien ne te dégoûte, tu dégoûtes tout le monde et que tu n'aimes que l'eau de vaisselle grasse.

Mais ils te calomnient.

Qu'ils te débarbouillent et tu auras bonne mine.

Tu te négliges par leur faute.

Comme on fait ton lit, tu te couches, et la malpropreté n'est que ta seconde nature.

le cochon et les perles

113

Dès qu'on le lâche au pré, le cochon se met à manger et son groin ne quitte plus la terre.

Il ne choisit pas l'herbe fine. Il attaque la première venue et pousse au hasard, devant lui, comme un soc ou comme une taupe aveugle, son nez infatigable.

Il ne s'occupe que d'arrondir un ventre qui prend déjà la forme du saloir, et jamais il n'a souci du temps qu'il fait.

Qu'importe que ses soies aient failli s'allumer tout à l'heure au soleil de midi, et qu'importe maintenant que ce nuage lourd, gonflé de grêle, s'étale et crève sur le pré.

La pie, il est vrai, d'un vol automatique se sauve; les dindes se cachent dans la haie, et le poulain puéril s'abrite sous un chêne.

Mais le cochon reste où il mange.

Il ne perd pas une bouchée.

Il ne remue pas, avec moins d'aise, la queue.

Tout criblé de grêlons, c'est à peine s'il grogne :

— Encore leurs sales perles!

les moutons

115

Ils reviennent des chaumes, où, depuis ce matin, ils paissaient, le nez à l'ombre de leur corps.

Selon les signes d'un berger indolent, le chien nécessaire attaque la bande du côté qu'il faut.

Elle tient toute la route, ondule d'un fossé à l'autre et déborde, ou tassée, unie, moelleuse, piétine le sol, à petits pas de vieilles femmes. Quand elle se met à courir, les pattes font le bruit des roseaux et criblent la poussière du chemin de nids d'abeilles.

Ce mouton frisé, bien garni, saute comme un ballot jeté en l'air, et du cornet de son oreille s'échappent des pastilles.

Cet autre a le vertige et heurte du genou sa tête mal vissée.

Ils envahissent le village. On dirait que c'est aujourd'hui leur fête et qu'avec pétulance, ils bêlent de joie par les rues.

Mais ils ne s'arrêtent pas au village, et je les vois reparaître, là-bas. Ils gagnent l'horizon. Par le coteau, ils montent, légers, vers le soleil. Ils s'en approchent et se couchent à distance...

Des traînards prennent, sur le ciel, une dernière forme imprévue, et rejoignent la troupe pelotonnée.

Un flocon se détache encore et plane, mousse blanche, puis fumée, vapeur, puis rien.

Il ne reste plus qu'une patte dehors. Elle s'allonge, elle s'effile comme une quenouille, à l'infini.

Les moutons frileux s'endorment autour du soleil las qui défait sa couronne et pique, jusqu'à demain, ses rayons dans leur laine.

LES MOUTONS. — Mée... Mée... Mée...
LE CHIEN DE BERGER. — Il n'y a pas de mais!

le bouc

121

Son odeur le précède. On ne le voit pas encore qu'elle est arrivée.

Il s'avance en tête du troupeau et les brebis le suivent, pêle-mêle, dans un nuage de poussière.

Il a des poils longs et secs qu'une raie partage sur le dos.

Il est moins fier de sa barbe que de sa taille, parce que la chèvre aussi porte une barbe sous le menton.

Quand il passe, les uns se bouchent le nez, les autres aiment ce goût-là.

Il ne regarde ni à droite ni à gauche : il marche raide, les oreilles pointues et la queue courte. Si les hommes l'ont chargé de leurs péchés, il n'en sait rien, et il laisse, sérieux, tomber un chapelet de crottes.

Alexandre est son nom, connu même des chiens.

La journée finie, le soleil disparu, il rentre au village, avec les moissonneurs, et ses cornes, fléchissant de vieillesse, prennent peu à peu la courbe des faucilles.

les lapins

127

Dans une moitié de futaille, Lenoir et Legris, les pattes au chaud sous la fourrure, mangent comme des vaches. Ils ne font qu'un seul repas qui dure toute la journée.

Si on tarde à leur jeter une herbe fraîche, ils rongent l'ancienne jusqu'à la racine, et la racine même occupe les dents.

Or il vient de leur tomber un pied de salade. Ensemble Lenoir et Legris se mettent après.

Nez à nez, ils s'évertuent, hochent la tête, et les oreilles trottent.

Quand il ne reste qu'une feuille, ils la prennent, chacun par un bout, et lut-

Vous croiriez qu'ils jouent, s'ils ne rient pas, et que, la feuille avalée, une caresse fraternelle unira les becs.

Mais Legris se sent faiblir. Depuis hier il a le gros ventre et une poche d'eau le ballonne. Vraiment il se bourrait trop. Bien qu'une feuille de salade passe sans qu'on ait faim, il n'en peut plus. Il lâche la feuille et se couche de côté, sur ses crottes, avec des convulsions brèves.

Le voilà rigide, les pattes écartées, comme pour une réclame d'armurier : *On tue net, on tue loin.*

Un instant Lenoir s'arrête de surprise. Assis en chandelier, le souffle doux, les lèvres jointes et l'œil cerclé de rose, il regarde.

Il a l'air d'un sorcier qui pénètre un mystère.

Ses deux oreilles droites marquent l'heure suprême.

Puis elles se cassent.

Et il achève la feuille de salade.

la souris

131

Comme à la clarté d'une lampe, je fais ma quotidienne page d'écriture, j'entends un léger bruit. Si je m'arrête, il cesse. Il recommence, dès que je gratte le papier.

C'est une souris qui s'éveille.

Je devine ses va-et-vient au bord du trou obscur où notre servante met ses torchons et ses brosses.

Elle saute par terre et trotte sur les carreaux de cuisine. Elle passe près de la cheminée, sous l'évier, se perd dans la vaisselle, et par une série de reconnaissances qu'elle pousse de plus en plus loin, elle se rapproche de moi.

Chaque fois que je pose mon porteplume, ce silence l'inquiète. Chaque fois que je m'en sers, elle croit peut-être qu'il y a une autre souris quelque part, et elle se rassure.

Puis je ne la vois plus. Elle est sous ma table, dans mes jambes. Elle circule d'un pied de chaise à l'autre. Elle frôle mes sabots, en mordille le bois, ou, hardiment, la voilà dessus!

Et il ne faut pas que je bouge la jambe, que je respire trop fort : elle filerait.

Mais il faut que je continue d'écrire, et de peur qu'elle ne m'abandonne à mon ennui de solitaire, j'écris des signes, des riens, petitement, menu, menu, comme elle grignote.

la belette

136

Pauvre, mais propre, distinguée, elle passe et repasse, par petits bonds, sur la route, et va, d'un fossé à l'autre, donner, de trou en trou, ses leçons au cachet.

le lézard

137

Fils spontané de la pierre fendue où je m'appuie, il me grimpe sur l'épaule. Il a cru que je continuais le mur parce que je reste immobile et que j'ai un paletot couleur de muraille. Ça flatte tout de même.

Le Mur. — Je ne sais quel frisson me passe sur le dos.
Le Lézard. — C'est moi.

le ver

140

En voilà un qui s'étire et s'allonge comme une belle nouille.

le ver luisant

141

Que se passe-t-il? Neuf heures du soir et il y a encore de la lumière chez lui.

la couleuvre

142

De quel ventre est-elle tombée, cette colique?

le serpent

143

Trop long.

l'escargot

145　　　　I

Casanier dans la saison des rhumes, son cou de girafe rentré, l'escargot bout comme un nez plein.

Il se promène dès les beaux jours, mais il ne sait marcher que sur la langue.

II

Mon petit camarade Abel jouait avec ses escargots.

Il en élève une pleine boîte et il a soin, pour les reconnaître, de numéroter au crayon la coquille.

S'il fait trop sec, les escargots dorment dans la boîte. Dès que la pluie menace, Abel les aligne dehors, et si elle tarde à tomber, il les réveille en versant dessus un pot d'eau. Et tous, sauf les mères qui couvent, dit-il, au fond de la boîte, se promènent sous la garde d'un chien appelé Barbare et qui est une lame de plomb qu'Abel pousse du doigt.

Comme je causais avec lui du mal que donne leur dressage, je m'aperçus qu'il me faisait signe que *non*, même quand il me répondait oui.

— Abel, lui dis-je, pourquoi ta tête remue-t-elle ainsi de droite et de gauche?

— C'est mon sucre, dit Abel.

— Quel sucre?

— Tiens, là.

Tandis qu'à quatre pattes, il ramenait le numéro 8 près de s'égarer, je vis au cou d'Abel, entre la peau et la chemise, un morceau de sucre qui pendait à un fil, comme une médaille.

— Maman me l'attache, dit-il, quand elle veut me punir.

— Ça te gêne?

— Ça gratte.

— Et ça cuit, hein! c'est tout rouge.

— Mais quand elle me pardonne, dit Abel, je le mange.

les grenouilles

149

Par brusques détentes, elles exercent leurs ressorts.

Elles sautent de l'herbe comme de lourdes gouttes d'huile frite.

Elles se posent, presse-papiers de bronze, sur les larges feuilles du nénuphar.

L'une se gorge d'air. On mettrait un sou, par sa bouche, dans la tirelire de son ventre.

Elles montent, comme des soupirs, de la vase.

Immobiles, elles semblent les gros yeux à fleur d'eau, les tumeurs de la mare plate.

Assises en tailleur, stupéfiées, elles bâillent au soleil couchant.

Puis, comme les camelots assourdissants des rues, elles crient les dernières nouvelles du jour.

Il y aura réception chez elles ce soir; les entendez-vous rincer leurs verres?

Parfois, elles happent un insecte.

Et d'autres ne s'occupent que d'amour.

Et toutes, elles tentent le pêcheur à la ligne.

Je casse, sans difficulté, une gaule. J'ai, piquée à mon paletot, une épingle que je recourbe en hameçon.

La ficelle ne me manque pas.

Mais il me faudrait encore un brin de laine, un bout de n'importe quoi rouge.

Je cherche sur moi, par terre, au ciel.

Je ne trouve rien et je regarde mélancoliquement ma boutonnière fendue, toute prête, que, sans reproche, on ne se hâte guère d'orner du ruban rouge.

le crapaud

151

Né d'une pierre, il vit sous une pierre et s'y creusera un tombeau.

Je le visite fréquemment, et chaque fois que je lève sa pierre, j'ai peur de le retrouver et peur qu'il n'y soit plus.

Il y est.

Caché dans ce gîte sec, propre, étroit, bien à lui, il l'occupe pleinement, gonflé comme une bourse d'avare.

Qu'une pluie le fasse sortir, il vient au-devant de moi. Quelques sauts lourds, et il s'arrête sur ses cuisses et me regarde de ses yeux rougis.

Si le monde injuste le traite en lépreux, je ne crains pas de m'accroupir près de lui et d'approcher du sien mon visage d'homme.

Puis je dompterai un reste de dégoût, et je te caresserai de ma main, crapaud!

On en avale dans la vie qui font plus mal au cœur.

Pourtant, hier, j'ai manqué de tact. Il fermentait et suintait, toutes ses verrues crevées.

— Mon pauvre ami, lui dis-je, je ne veux pas te faire de peine, mais, Dieu! que tu es laid!

Il ouvrit sa bouche puérile et sans dents, à l'haleine chaude, et me répondit avec un léger accent anglais :

— Et toi?

l'araignée

157

Une petite main noire et poilue crispée sur des cheveux.

Toute la nuit, au nom de la lune, elle appose ses scellés.

le cafard

159

Noir et collé comme un trou de serrure.

la chenille

161

Elle sort d'une touffe d'herbe qui l'avait cachée pendant la chaleur. Elle traverse l'allée de sable à grandes ondulations. Elle se garde d'y faire halte et un moment elle se croit perdue dans une trace de sabot du jardinier.

Arrivée aux fraises, elle se repose, lève le nez de droite et de gauche pour flairer; puis elle repart et sous les feuilles, sur les feuilles, elle sait maintenant où elle va.

Quelle belle chenille, grasse, velue, fourrée, brune avec des points d'or et ses yeux noirs!

Guidée par l'odorat, elle se trémousse et se fronce comme un épais sourcil.

Elle s'arrête au bas d'un rosier.

De ses fines agrafes, elle tâte l'écorce rude, balance sa petite tête de chien nouveau-né et se décide à grimper.

Et, cette fois, vous diriez qu'elle avale péniblement chaque longueur de chemin par déglutition.

Tout en haut du rosier, s'épanouit une rose au teint de candide fillette. Ses parfums qu'elle prodigue la grisent. Elle ne se défie de personne. Elle laisse monter par sa tige la première chenille venue. Elle l'accueille comme un cadeau.

Et, pressentant qu'il fera froid cette nuit, elle est bien aise de se mettre un boa autour du cou.

le papillon

164

Ce billet doux plié en deux cherche une adresse de fleur.

la guêpe

165

Elle finira pourtant par s'abîmer la taille!

la demoiselle

169

Elle soigne son ophtalmie.

D'un bord à l'autre de la rivière, elle ne fait que tremper dans l'eau fraîche ses yeux gonflés.

Et elle grésille, comme si elle volait à l'électricité.

le grillon

171

C'est l'heure où, las d'errer, l'insecte nègre revient de promenade et répare avec soin le désordre de son domaine.

D'abord il ratisse ses étroites allées de sable.

Il fait du bran de scie qu'il écarte au seuil de sa retraite.

Il lime la racine de cette grande herbe propre à le harceler.

Il se repose.

Puis il remonte sa minuscule montre.

A-t-il fini? est-elle cassée? Il se repose encore un peu.

Il rentre chez lui et ferme sa porte.

Longtemps il tourne sa clef dans la serrure délicate.

Et il écoute :

Point d'alarme dehors.

Mais il ne se trouve pas en sûreté.

Et comme par une chaînette dont la poulie grince, il descend jusqu'au fond de la terre.

On n'entend plus rien.

Dans la campagne muette, les peupliers se dressent comme des doigts en l'air et désignent la lune.

la sauterelle

175

Serait-ce le gendarme des insectes?

Tout le jour, elle saute et s'acharne aux trousses d'invisibles braconniers qu'elle n'attrape jamais.

Les plus hautes herbes ne l'arrêtent pas.

Rien ne lui fait peur, car elle a des bottes de sept lieues, un cou de taureau, le front génial, le ventre d'une carène, des ailes en celluloïd, des cornes diaboliques et un grand sabre au derrière.

Comme on ne peut avoir les vertus d'un gendarme sans les vices, il faut bien le dire, la sauterelle chique.

Si je mens, poursuis-la de tes doigts, joue avec elle à quatre coins, et quand tu l'auras saisie, entre deux bonds, sur une feuille de luzerne, observe sa bouche : par ses terribles mandibules, elle sécrète une mousse noire comme du jus de tabac.

Mais déjà tu ne la tiens plus. Sa rage de sauter la reprend. Le monstre vert t'échappe d'un brusque effort et, fragile, démontable, te laisse une petite cuisse dans la main.

les fourmis

176

Chacune d'elles ressemble au chiffre 3.

Et il y en a! il y en a!

Il y en a 333333333333... jusqu'à l'infini.

la fourmi et le perdreau

177

Une fourmi tombe dans une ornière où il a plu et elle va se noyer, quand un perdreau, qui buvait, la pince du bec et la sauve.

— Je vous le revaudrai, dit la fourmi.

— Nous ne sommes plus, répond le perdreau sceptique, au temps de La Fontaine. Non que je doute de votre gratitude, mais comment piqueriez-vous au talon le chasseur prêt à me tuer! Les chasseurs aujourd'hui ne marchent point pieds nus.

La fourmi ne perd pas sa peine à discuter et elle se hâte de rejoindre ses sœurs qui suivent toutes le même chemin, semblables à des perles noires qu'on enfile.

Or le chasseur n'est pas loin.

Il se reposait, sur le flanc, à l'ombre d'un arbre. Il aperçoit le perdreau piétant et picotant à travers le chaume. Il se dresse et veut tirer, mais il a des fourmis dans le bras droit. Il ne peut lever son arme. Le bras retombe inerte et le perdreau n'attend pas qu'il se dégourdisse.

la puce

180

Un grain de tabac à ressort.

l'écureuil

181

Du panache! du panache! oui, sans doute; mais, mon petit ami, ce n'est pas là que ça se met.

singes...

183

Allez voir les singes (maudits gamins, ils ont tout déchiré leur fond de culotte!) grimper, danser au soleil neuf, se fâcher, se gratter, éplucher des choses, et boire avec une grâce primitive, tandis que de leurs yeux, troubles parfois mais pas longtemps, s'échappent des lueurs vite éteintes.

Allez voir les flamants qui marchent sur des pincettes, de peur de mouiller, dans l'eau du bassin, leurs jupons roses; les cygnes et la vaniteuse plomberie de leur col; l'autruche, ses ailes de poussin, et sa casquette de chef de gare responsable; les cigognes qui haussent tout le temps des épaules (à la fin, ça ne signifie plus rien); le marabout frileux dans sa pauvre jaquette, les pingouins en macfarlane; le pélican qui tient son bec comme un sabre de bois, et les perruches, dont les plus apprivoisées le sont moins que leur gardien lui-même qui finit par nous prendre une pièce de dix sous dans la main.

Allez voir le yack lourd de pensées préhistoriques; la girafe qui nous montre, par-dessus les barreaux de la grille, sa tête au bout d'une pique; l'éléphant qui traîne ses chaussons devant sa porte, courbé, le nez bas: il disparaît presque dans le sac d'une culotte trop remontée, et, derrière, un petit bout de corde pend.

Allez donc voir le porc-épic garni de porte-plume bien gênants pour lui et son amie; le zèbre, modèle à transparent de tous les autres zèbres; la panthère descendue au pied de son lit; l'ours qui nous amuse et ne s'amuse guère, et le lion qui bâille, à nous faire bâiller.

le cerf

191

J'entrai au bois par un bout de l'allée, comme il arrivait par l'autre bout.

Je crus d'abord qu'une personne étrangère s'avançait avec une plante sur la tête.

Puis je distinguai le petit arbre nain, aux branches écartées et sans feuilles.

Enfin le cerf apparut net et nous nous arrêtâmes tous deux.

Je lui dis:

— Approche. Ne crains rien. Si j'ai un fusil, c'est par contenance, pour imiter les hommes qui se prennent au sérieux. Je ne m'en sers jamais et je laisse ses cartouches dans leur tiroir.

Le cerf écoutait et flairait mes paroles. Dès que je me tus, il n'hésita point: ses jambes remuèrent comme des tiges qu'un souffle d'air croise et décroise. Il s'enfuit.

— Quel dommage! lui criai-je. Je rêvais déjà que nous faisions route ensemble. Moi, je t'offrais, de ma main, les herbes que tu aimes, et toi, d'un pas de promenade, tu portais mon fusil couché sur ta ramure.

le goujon

197

Il remonte le courant d'eau vive et suit le chemin que tracent les cailloux: car il n'aime ni la vase, ni les herbes.

Il aperçoit une bouteille couchée sur un lit de sable. Elle n'est pleine que d'eau. J'ai oublié à dessein d'y mettre une amorce. Le goujon tourne autour, cherche l'entrée et le voilà pris.

Je ramène la bouteille et rejette le goujon.

Plus haut, il entend du bruit. Loin de fuir, il s'approche, par curiosité. C'est moi qui m'amuse, piétine dans l'eau et remue le fond avec une perche, au bord d'un filet. Le goujon têtu veut passer par une maille. Il y reste.

Je lève le filet et rejette le goujon.

Plus bas, une brusque secousse tend ma ligne et le bouchon bicolore file entre deux eaux.

Je tire et c'est encore lui.

Je le décroche de l'hameçon et le rejette.

Cette fois, je ne l'aurai plus.

Il est là, immobile, à mes pieds, sous l'eau claire. Je distingue sa tête élargie, son gros œil stupide et sa paire de barbillons.

Il bâille, la lèvre déchirée, et il respire fort, après une telle émotion.

Mais rien ne le corrige.

Je laisse de nouveau tremper ma ligne avec le même ver.

Et aussitôt le goujon mord.

Lequel de nous deux se lassera le premier?

Décidément, ils ne veulent pas mordre. Ils ne savent donc pas que c'est aujourd'hui l'ouverture de la pêche!

la baleine

198

Elle a bien dans la bouche de quoi se faire un corset, mais avec ce tour de taille!...

au jardin

199

La Bêche. — *Fac et spera.*
La Pioche. — Moi aussi.

Les Fleurs. — Fera-t-il soleil aujourd'hui?
Le Tournesol. — Oui, si je veux.
L'Arrosoir. — Pardon, si je veux, il pleuvra, et, si j'ôte ma pomme, à torrents.

Le Rosier. — Oh! quel vent!
Le Tuteur. — Je suis là.

La Framboise. — Pourquoi les roses ont-elles des épines? ça ne se mange pas, une rose.
La Carpe du vivier. — Bien dit! C'est parce qu'on me mange que je pique, moi, avec mes arêtes.
Le Chardon. — Oui, mais trop tard.

LA ROSE. — Me trouves-tu belle?

LE FRELON. — Il faudrait voir les dessous.

LA ROSE. — Entre.

L'ABEILLE. — Du courage! Tout le monde me dit que je travaille bien. J'espère, à la fin du mois, passer chef de rayon.

LES VIOLETTES. — Nous sommes toutes officiers d'académie.

LES VIOLETTES BLANCHES. — Raison de plus pour être modestes, mes sœurs.

LE POIREAU. — Sans doute. Est-ce que je me vante?

L'ÉPINARD. — C'est moi qui suis l'oseille.

L'OSEILLE. — Mais non, c'est moi.

L'ÉCHALOTE. — Oh! que ça sent mauvais!

L'AIL. — Je parie que c'est encore l'œillet.

L'ASPERGE. — Mon petit doigt me dit tout.

LA POMME DE TERRE. — Je crois que je viens de faire mes petits.

LE POMMIER, *au Poirier d'en face.* — C'est ta poire, ta poire, ta poire..., c'est ta poire que je voudrais produire.

les coquelicots

202

Ils éclatent dans le blé, comme une armée de petits soldats; mais d'un bien plus beau rouge, ils sont inoffensifs.

Leur épée, c'est un épi.

C'est le vent qui les fait courir, et chaque coquelicot s'attarde, quand il veut, au bord du sillon, avec le bleuet, sa payse.

la vigne

202

Tous ses ceps, l'échalas droit, sont au port d'armes.

Qu'attendent-ils? le raisin ne sortira pas encore cette année, et les feuilles de vigne ne servent plus qu'aux statues.

le martin-pêcheur

203

Ça n'a pas mordu, ce soir, mais je rapporte une rare émotion.

Comme je tenais ma perche de ligne tendue, un martin-pêcheur est venu s'y poser.

Nous n'avons pas d'oiseau plus éclatant.

Il semblait une grosse fleur bleue au bout d'une longue tige. La perche pliait sous le poids. Je ne respirais plus, tout fier d'être pris pour un arbre par un martin-pêcheur.

Et je suis sûr qu'il ne s'est pas envolé de peur, mais qu'il a cru qu'il ne faisait que passer d'une branche à une autre.

le nid
de chardonnerets

207

Il y avait, sur une branche fourchue de notre cerisier, un nid de chardonnerets joli à voir, rond, parfait, tout crins au dehors, tout duvet au dedans, et quatre petits venaient d'y éclore. Je dis à mon père :

— J'ai presque envie de les prendre pour les élever.

Mon père m'avait expliqué souvent que c'est un crime de mettre des oiseaux en cage. Mais, cette fois, las sans doute de répéter la même chose, il ne trouva rien à me répondre. Quelques jours après, je lui dis :

— Si je veux, ce sera facile. Je placerai d'abord le nid dans une cage, j'attacherai la cage au cerisier et la mère nourrira les petits par les barreaux jusqu'à ce qu'ils n'aient plus besoin d'elle.

Mon père ne me dit pas ce qu'il pensait de ce moyen.

C'est pourquoi j'installai le nid dans une cage, la cage sur le cerisier et ce que j'avais prévu arriva : les vieux chardonnerets, sans hésiter, apportèrent aux petits des pleins becs de chenilles. Et mon père observait de loin, amusé comme moi, leur va-et-vient fleuri, leur vol teint de rouge sang et de jaune soufre.

Je dis un soir :

— Les petits sont assez drus. S'ils étaient libres, ils s'envoleraient. Qu'ils passent une dernière nuit en famille et demain je les porterai à la maison, je les pendrai à ma fenêtre, et je te prie de croire qu'il n'y aura pas beaucoup de chardonnerets au monde mieux soignés.

Mon père ne me dit pas le contraire.

Le lendemain je trouvai la cage vide. Mon père était là, témoin de ma stupeur.

— Je ne suis pas curieux, dis-je, mais je voudrais bien savoir quel est l'imbécile qui a ouvert la porte de cette cage!

la cage sans oiseau

208

Félix ne comprend pas qu'on tienne des oiseaux prisonniers dans une cage.

— De même, dit-il, que c'est un crime de cueillir une fleur, et, personnellement, je ne veux la respirer que sur sa tige, de même les oiseaux sont faits pour voler.

Cependant il achète une cage; il l'accroche à sa fenêtre. Il y dépose un nid d'ouate, une soucoupe de graines, une tasse d'eau pure et renouvelable. Il y suspend une balançoire et une petite glace.

Et comme on l'interroge avec surprise :

— Je me félicite de ma générosité, dit-il, chaque fois que je regarde cette cage. Je pourrais y mettre un oiseau et je la laisse vide. Si je voulais, telle grive brune, tel bouvreuil pimpant, qui sautille, ou tel autre de nos oiseaux variés serait esclave. Mais grâce à moi, l'un d'eux au moins reste libre. C'est toujours ça.

la bergeronnette

209

Elle court autant qu'elle vole, et toujours dans nos jambes, familière, imprenable, elle nous défie, avec ses petits cris, de marcher sur sa queue.

le loriot

209

Je lui dis :

— Rends-moi cette cerise, tout de suite.

— Bien, répond le loriot.

Il rend la cerise et, avec la cerise, les trois cent mille larves d'insectes nuisibles qu'il avale dans une année.

le serin

210

Quelle idée ai-je eue d'acheter cet oiseau?

L'oiselier me dit : « C'est un mâle. Attendez une semaine qu'il s'habitue, et il chantera. »

Or l'oiseau s'obstine à se taire et il fait tout de travers.

Dès que je remplis son gobelet de graines, il les pille du bec et les jette aux quatre vents.

J'attache, avec une ficelle, un biscuit entre deux barreaux. Il ne mange que la ficelle. Il repousse et frappe, comme un marteau, le biscuit et le biscuit tombe.

Il se baigne dans son eau pure et il boit dans sa baignoire. Il crotte au petit bonheur dans les deux.

Il s'imagine que l'échaudé est une pâte toute prête où les oiseaux de son espèce se creusent des nids et il s'y blottit d'instinct.

Il n'a pas encore compris l'utilité des feuilles de salade et ne s'amuse qu'à les déchirer.

Quand il pique une graine pour de bon, pour l'avaler, il fait peine. Il la roule d'un coin à l'autre du bec, et la presse et l'écrase, et tortille sa tête, comme un petit vieux qui n'a plus de dents.

Son bout de sucre ne lui sert jamais. Est-ce une pierre qui dépasse, un balcon ou une table peu pratique?

Il lui préfère ses morceaux de bois. Il en a deux qui se superposent et se croisent et je m'écœure à le regarder sauter. Il égale la stupidité mécanique d'une pendule qui ne marquerait rien. Pour quel plaisir saute-t-il ainsi, sautillant par quelle nécessité?

S'il se repose de sa gymnastique morne, perché d'une patte sur un bâton qu'il étrangle, il cherche de l'autre patte, machinalement, le même bâton.

Aussitôt que, l'hiver venu, on allume le poêle, il croit que c'est le printemps, l'époque de sa mue et il se dépouille de ses plumes.

L'éclat de ma lampe trouble ses nuits, désordonne ses heures de sommeil. Il se couche au crépuscule. Je laisse les ténèbres s'épaissir autour de lui. Peut-être rêve-t-il? Brusquement, j'approche la lampe de sa cage. Il rouvre les yeux. Quoi! c'est déjà le jour? Et vite il recommence de s'agiter, danser, cribler une feuille, et il écarte sa queue en éventail, décolle ses ailes.

Mais je souffle la lampe et je regrette de ne pas voir sa mine ahurie.

J'ai bientôt assez de cet oiseau muet qui ne vit qu'à rebours, et je le mets dehors par la fenêtre... Il ne sait pas plus se servir de la liberté que d'une cage. On va le reprendre avec la main.

Qu'on se garde de me le rapporter.

Non seulement je n'offre aucune récompense, mais je jure que je ne connais pas cet oiseau.

hirondelles

213

Elles me donnent ma leçon de chaque jour.

Elles pointillent l'air de petits cris.

Elles tracent une raie droite, posent une virgule au bout, et, brusquement vont à la ligne.

Elles mettent entre folles parenthèses la maison où j'habite.

Trop vives pour que la pièce d'eau du jardin prenne copie de leur vol, elles montent de la cave au grenier.

D'une plume d'aile légère, elles bouclent d'inimitables parafes.

Puis, deux à deux, en accolade, elles se joignent, se mêlent, et, sur le bleu du ciel, elles font tache d'encre.

Mais l'œil d'un ami peut seul les suivre, et si vous savez le grec et le latin, moi je sais lire l'hébreu que décrivent dans l'air les hirondelles de cheminée.

LE PINSON. — Je trouve l'hirondelle stupide : elle croit qu'une cheminée, c'est un arbre.

LA CHAUVE-SOURIS. — Et on a beau dire, de nous deux c'est elle qui vole le plus mal : en plein jour, elle ne fait que se tromper de chemin; si elle volait la nuit, comme moi, elle se tuerait à chaque instant.

chauves-souris

215

La nuit s'use à force de servir.

Elle ne s'use point par le haut, dans ses étoiles. Elle s'use comme une robe qui traîne à terre, entre les cailloux et les arbres, jusqu'au fond des tunnels malsains et des caves humides.

Il n'est pas de coin où ne pénètre un pan de nuit. L'épine le crève, les froids le gercent, la boue le gâte. Et chaque matin, quand la nuit remonte, des loques s'en détachent, accrochées au hasard.

Ainsi naissent les chauves-souris.

Et elles doivent à cette origine de ne pouvoir supporter l'éclat du jour.

Le soleil couché, quand nous prenons le frais, elles se décollent des vieilles poutres où, léthargiques, elles pendaient d'une griffe.

Leur vol gauche nous inquiète. D'une aile baleinée et sans plumes, elles palpitent autour de nous. Elles se dirigent moins avec d'inutiles yeux blessés qu'avec l'oreille.

Mon amie cache son visage, et moi je détourne la tête par peur du choc impur.

On dit qu'avec plus d'ardeur que notre amour même, elles nous suceraient le sang jusqu'à la mort.

Comme on exagère!

Elles ne sont pas méchantes. Elles ne nous touchent jamais.

Filles de la nuit, elles ne détestent que les lumières, et, du frôlement de leurs petits châles funèbres, elles cherchent des bougies à souffler.

la pie

216

Il lui reste toujours, du dernier hiver, un peu de neige.

Elle sautille à pieds joints par terre, puis, de son vol droit et mécanique, elle se dirige vers un arbre.

Quelquefois elle le manque et ne peut s'arrêter que sur l'arbre voisin.

Commune, si dédaignée qu'elle semble immortelle, en habit dès le matin pour bavarder jusqu'au soir, insupportable avec sa queue-de-pie, c'est notre oiseau le plus français.

LA PIE. — Cacacacacaca.
LA GRENOUILLE. — Qu'est-ce qu'elle dit?
LA PIE. — Je ne dis pas, je chante.
LA GRENOUILLE. — Couac!
LA TAUPE. — Taisez-vous donc là-haut, on ne s'entend plus travailler!

merle!

219

Dans mon jardin il y a un vieux noyer presque mort qui fait peur aux petits oiseaux. Seul un oiseau noir habite ses dernières feuilles.

Mais le reste du jardin est plein de jeunes arbres fleuris où nichent des oiseaux gais, vifs et de toutes les couleurs.

Et il semble que ces jeunes arbres se moquent du vieux noyer. A chaque instant, ils lui lancent, comme des paroles taquines, une volée d'oiseaux babillards.

Tour à tour, pierrots, martins, mésanges et pinsons le harcèlent. Ils choquent de l'aile la pointe de ses branches. L'air crépite de leurs cris menus; puis ils se sauvent, et c'est une autre bande importune qui part des jeunes arbres.

Tant qu'elle peut, elle nargue, piaille, siffle et s'égosille.

Ainsi de l'aube au crépuscule, comme des mots railleurs, pinsons, mésanges, martins et pierrots s'échappent des jeunes arbres vers le vieux noyer.

Mais parfois il s'impatiente, il remue ses dernières feuilles, lâche son oiseau noir et répond :

Merle!

LE GEAI. — Toujours en noir, vilain merle!

LE MERLE. — Monsieur le sous-préfet, je n'ai que ça à me mettre.

l'alouette

221

Je n'ai jamais vu d'alouette et je me lève inutilement avec l'aurore. L'alouette n'est pas un oiseau de la terre.

Depuis ce matin, je foule les mottes et les herbes sèches.

Des bandes de moineaux gris ou de chardonnerets peints à vif flottent sur les haies d'épines.

Le geai passe la revue des arbres dans un costume officiel.

Une caille rase les luzernes et trace au cordeau la ligne droite de son vol.

Derrière le berger qui tricote mieux qu'une femme, les moutons se suivent et se ressemblent.

Et tout s'imprègne d'une lumière si neuve que le corbeau, qui ne présage rien de bon, fait sourire.

Mais écoutez comme j'écoute.

Entendez-vous quelque part, là-haut, piler dans une coupe d'or des morceaux de cristal?

Qui peut me dire où l'alouette chante?

Si je regarde en l'air, le soleil brûle mes yeux.

Il me faut renoncer à la voir.

L'alouette vit au ciel, et c'est le seul oiseau du ciel qui chante jusqu'à nous.

l'épervier

223

Il décrit d'abord des ronds sur le village.

Il n'était qu'une mouche, un grain de suie.

Il grossit à mesure que son vol se resserre.

Parfois il demeure immobile. Les volailles donnent des signes d'inquiétude. Les pigeons rentrent au toit. Une poule, d'un cri bref, rappelle ses petits, et on entend cacarder les oies vigilantes d'une basse-cour à l'autre.

L'épervier hésite et plane à la même hauteur. Peut-être n'en veut-il qu'au coq du clocher.

On le croirait pendu au ciel, par un fil.

Brusquement le fil casse, l'épervier tombe, sa victime choisie. C'est l'heure d'un drame ici-bas.

Mais, à la surprise générale, il s'arrête avant de toucher terre, comme s'il manquait de poids, et il remonte d'un coup d'aile.

Il a vu que je le guette de ma porte, et que je cache, derrière moi, quelque chose de long qui brille.

le corbeau

226

Quoi? quoi? quoi?
— Rien.

les perdrix

227

La perdrix et le laboureur vivent en paix, lui derrière sa charrue, elle dans la luzerne voisine, à la distance qu'il faut l'un de l'autre pour ne pas se gêner. La perdrix connaît la voix du laboureur, elle ne le redoute pas quand il crie ou qu'il jure.

Que la charrue grince, que le bœuf tousse et que l'âne se mette à braire, elle sait que ce n'est rien.

Et cette paix dure jusqu'à ce que je la trouble.

Mais j'arrive et la perdrix s'envole, le laboureur n'est pas tranquille, le bœuf non plus, l'âne non plus. Je tire, et au fracas d'un importun, toute la nature se désordonne.

Ces perdrix, je les lève d'abord dans une éteule, puis je les relève dans une luzerne, puis je les relève dans un pré, puis le long d'une haie, puis à la corne d'un bois, puis...

Et tout à coup je m'arrête, en sueur, et je m'écrie :

— Ah! les sauvages, me font-elles courir!

De loin, j'ai aperçu quelque chose au pied d'un arbre, au milieu du pré.

Je m'approche de la haie et je regarde par-dessus.

Il me semble qu'un col d'oiseau se dresse à l'ombre de l'arbre. Aussitôt mes battements de cœur s'accélèrent. Il ne peut y avoir dans cette herbe, que des perdrix. Par un signal familier, la mère, en m'entendant, les a fait se coucher à plat. Elle-même s'est baissée. Son col seul reste droit et elle veille. Mais j'hésite, car le col ne remue pas et j'ai peur de me tromper, de tirer sur une racine.

Çà et là, autour de l'arbre, des taches jaunes, perdrix ou mottes de terre, achèvent de me troubler la vue.

Si je fais partir les perdrix, les branches de l'arbre m'empêcheront de tirer au vol, et j'aime mieux, en tirant par terre, commettre ce que les chasseurs sérieux appellent un assassinat.

Mais ce que je prends pour un col de perdrix ne remue toujours pas.

Longtemps j'épie.

Si c'est bien une perdrix, elle est admirable d'immobilité et de vigilance, et toutes les autres, par leur façon de lui obéir, méritent cette gardienne. Pas une ne bouge.

Je fais une feinte. Je me cache tout entier derrière la haie et je cesse d'observer, car tant que je vois la perdrix, elle me voit.

Maintenant nous sommes tous invisibles, dans un silence de mort.

Puis, de nouveau, je regarde.

Oh! cette fois, je suis sûr! La perdrix a cru à ma disparition. Le col s'est haussé et le mouvement qu'elle fait pour le raccourcir la dénonce.

J'applique lentement à mon épaule ma crosse de fusil...

Le soir, las et repu, avant de m'endormir d'un sommeil giboyeux, je pense aux perdrix que j'ai chassées tout le jour, et j'imagine la nuit qu'elles passent.

Elles sont affolées.

Pourquoi en manque-t-il à l'appel?

Pourquoi en est-il qui souffrent et qui, becquetant leurs blessures, ne peuvent tenir en place?

Et pourquoi s'est-on mis à leur faire peur à toutes?

A peine se posent-elles maintenant, que celle qui guette sonne l'alarme. Il faut repartir, quitter l'herbe ou l'éteule.

Elles ne font que se sauver, et elles s'effraient même des bruits dont elles avaient l'habitude.

Elles ne s'ébattent plus, ne mangent plus, ne dorment plus.

Elles n'y comprennent rien.

Si la plume qui tombe d'une perdrix blessée venait se piquer d'elle-même à mon chapeau de fier chasseur, je ne trouverais pas que c'est exagéré.

Dès qu'il pleut trop ou qu'il fait trop sec, que mon chien ne sent plus, que je tire mal et que les perdrix deviennent inabordables, je me crois en état de légitime défense.

Il y a des oiseaux, la pie, le geai, le merle, la grive, avec lesquels un chasseur qui se respecte ne se bat pas, et je me respecte.

Je n'aime me battre qu'avec les perdrix. Elles sont si rusées!

Leurs ruses, c'est de partir de loin, mais on les rattrape et on les corrige.

C'est d'attendre que le chasseur ait passé, mais derrière lui elles s'envolent trop tôt et il se retourne.

C'est de se cacher dans une luzerne profonde, mais il y va tout droit.

C'est de faire un crochet au vol, mais ainsi elles se rapprochent.

C'est de courir au lieu de voler, et elles courent plus vite que l'homme, mais il y a le chien.

C'est de s'appeler quand on les divise, mais elles appellent aussi le chasseur et rien ne lui est plus agréable que leur chant.

Déjà ce couple de jeunes commençait de vivre à part. Je les surpris, le soir, au bord d'un labouré. Elles s'envolèrent si étroitement jointes, aile dessus, aile dessous je peux dire, que le coup de fusil qui tua l'une démonta l'autre.

L'une ne vit rien et ne sentit rien, mais l'autre eut le temps de voir sa compagne morte et de se sentir mourir près d'elle.

Toutes deux, au même endroit de la terre, elles ont laissé un peu d'amour, un peu de sang et quelques plumes.

Chasseur, d'un coup de fusil tu as fait deux beaux coups : va les conter à ta famille.

Ces deux vieilles de l'année dernière dont la couvée avait été détruite, ne s'aimaient pas moins que des jeunes.

Je les voyais toujours ensemble. Elles étaient habiles à m'éviter et je ne m'acharnais pas à leur poursuite. C'est par hasard que j'en ai tué une. Et puis j'ai cherché l'autre, pour la tuer, elle aussi, par pitié!

Celle-ci a une patte cassée qui pend, comme si je la retenais par un fil.

Celle-là suit d'abord les autres jusqu'à ce que ses ailes la trahissent; elle s'abat, et elle piète; elle court tant qu'elle peut, devant le chien, légère et à demi hors des sillons.

Celle-ci a reçu un grain de plomb dans la tête. Elle se détache des autres. Elle pointe en l'air, étourdie, elle monte plus haut que les arbres, plus haut qu'un coq de clocher, vers le soleil. Et le chasseur, plein d'angoisse, la perd de vue, quand elle cède enfin au poids de sa tête lourde. Elle ferme ses ailes, et va piquer du bec le sol, là-bas, comme une flèche.

Celle-là tombe, sans faire ouf! comme un chiffon qu'on jette au nez du chien pour le dresser.

Celle-là, au coup de feu, oscille comme une petite barque et chavire.

On ne sait pas pourquoi celle-ci est morte, tant la blessure est secrète sous les plumes.

Je fourre vite celle-là dans ma poche, comme si j'avais peur d'être vu, de me voir.

Mais il faut que j'étrangle celle qui ne veut pas mourir. Entre mes doigts, elle griffe l'air, elle ouvre le bec, sa fine langue palpite, et sur ses yeux, dit Homère, descend l'ombre de la mort.

Là-bas, le paysan lève la tête à mon coup de feu et me regarde.

C'est un juge, cet homme de travail; il va me parler; il va me faire honte d'une voix grave.

Mais non : tantôt c'est un paysan jaloux qui bisque de ne pas chasser comme moi, tantôt c'est un brave paysan que j'amuse et qui m'indique où sont allées mes perdrix.

Jamais ce n'est l'interprète indigné de la nature.

Je rentre ce matin, après cinq heures de marche, la carnassière vide, la tête basse et le fusil lourd. Il fait une chaleur d'orage et mon chien, éreinté, va devant moi, à petits pas, suit les haies, et fréquemment, s'assied à l'ombre d'un arbre où il m'attend.

Soudain, comme je traverse une luzerne fraîche, il tombe ou plutôt il s'aplatit en arrêt : c'est un arrêt ferme, une immobilité de végétal. Seuls les poils du bout de sa queue tremblent. Il y a, je le jurerais, des perdrix sous son nez. Elles sont là, collées les unes aux autres, à l'abri du vent et du soleil. Elles voient le chien, elles me voient, elles me reconnaissent peut-être, et terrifiées, elles ne partent pas.

Réveillé de ma torpeur, je suis prêt et j'attends.

Mon chien et moi, nous ne bougerons pas les premiers.

Brusquement et simultanément, les perdrix partent : toujours collées, elles ne font qu'une, et je flanque dans le tas mon coup de fusil comme un coup de poing. L'une d'elles, assommée, pirouette. Le chien saute dessus et me rapporte une loque sanglante, une moitié de perdrix. Le coup de poing a emporté le reste.

Allons! nous ne sommes pas bredouille! Le chien gambade et je me dandine d'orgueil.

Ah! je mériterais un bon coup de fusil dans les fesses!

la bécasse

234

Il ne restait, d'un soleil d'avril, que des lueurs roses aux nuages qui ne bougeaient plus, comme arrivés.

La nuit montait du sol et nous vêtait peu à peu, dans la clairière étroite où mon père attendait les bécasses.

Debout près de lui, je ne distinguais nettement que sa figure. Plus grand que moi, il me voyait à peine, et le chien soufflait, invisible à nos pieds.

Les grives se dépêchaient de rentrer au bois et le merle jetait son cri guttural, cette espèce de hennissement qui est un ordre à tous les oiseaux de se taire et de dormir.

La bécasse allait bientôt quitter ses retraites de feuilles mortes et s'élever. Quand il fait doux, comme ce soir-là, elle s'attarde, avant de gagner la plaine. Elle tourne sur le bois et se cherche une compagne. On devine, à son appel léger, qu'elle s'approche ou s'éloigne. Elle passe d'un vol lourd entre les gros chênes et son long bec pend si bas qu'elle semble se promener en l'air avec une petite canne.

Comme j'écoutais et regardais en tous sens, mon père brusquement fit feu, mais il ne suivit pas le chien qui s'élançait.

— Tu l'as manquée? lui dis-je.

— Je n'ai pas tiré, dit-il. Mon fusil vient de partir dans mes mains.

— Tout seul?

— Oui.

— Ah!... une branche peut-être?

— Je ne sais pas.

Je l'entendais ôter sa cartouche vide.

— Comment le tenais-tu?

N'avait-il pas compris?

— Je te demande de quel côté était le canon?

Comme il ne répondait plus, je n'osais plus parler. Enfin je lui dis :

— Tu aurais pu tuer... le chien.

— Allons-nous-en, dit mon père.

fermeture de la chasse

237

C'est une pauvre journée, grise et courte, comme rognée à ses deux bouts.

Vers midi, le soleil maussade essaie de percer la brume et entr'ouvre un œil pâle tout de suite refermé.

Je marche au hasard. Mon fusil m'est inutile, et le chien, si fou d'ordinaire, ne s'écarte pas.

L'eau de la rivière est d'une transparence qui fait mal : si on y plongeait les doigts, elle couperait comme une vitre cassée.

Dans l'éteule, à chacun de mes pas jaillit une alouette engourdie. Elles se réunissent, tourbillonnent et leur vol trouble à peine l'air gelé.

Là-bas, des congrégations de corbeaux déterrent du bec des semences d'automne.

Trois perdrix se dressent au milieu d'un pré dont l'herbe rase ne les abrite plus.

Comme les voilà grandies! Ce sont de vraies dames maintenant. Elles écoutent, inquiètes. Je les ai bien vues, mais je les laisse tranquilles et m'éloigne. Et quelque part, sans doute, un lièvre qui tremblait se rassure et remet son nez au bord du gîte.

Tout le long de cette haie (çà et là une dernière feuille bat de l'aile comme un oiseau dont la patte est prise), un merle fuit à mon approche, va se cacher plus loin, puis ressort sous le nez du chien et, sans risque, se moque de nous.

Peu à peu, la brume s'épaissit. Je me croirais perdu. Mon fusil n'est plus, dans mes mains, qu'un bâton qui peut éclater. D'où partent ce bruit vague, ce bêlement, ce son de cloche, ce cri humain?

Il faut rentrer. Par une route déjà effacée, je retourne au village. Lui seul connaît son nom. D'humbles paysans l'habitent, que personne ne vient jamais voir, excepté moi.

une famille d'arbres

239

C'est après avoir traversé une plaine brûlée de soleil que je les rencontre.

Ils ne demeurent pas au bord de la route, à cause du bruit. Ils habitent les champs incultes, sur une source connue des oiseaux seuls.

De loin, ils semblent impénétrables. Dès que j'approche, leurs troncs se desserrent. Ils m'accueillent avec prudence. Je peux me reposer, me rafraîchir, mais je devine qu'ils m'observent et se défient.

Ils vivent en famille, les plus âgés au milieu et les petits, ceux dont les premières feuilles viennent de naître, un peu partout, sans jamais s'écarter.

Ils mettent longtemps à mourir, et ils gardent les morts debout jusqu'à la chute en poussière.

Ils se flattent de leurs longues branches, pour s'assurer qu'ils sont tous là, comme les aveugles. Ils gesticulent de colère si le vent s'essouffle à les déraciner. Mais entre eux aucune dispute. Ils ne murmurent que d'accord.

Je sens qu'ils doivent être ma vraie famille. J'oublierai vite l'autre. Ces arbres m'adopteront peu à peu, et pour le mériter j'apprends ce qu'il faut savoir :

Je sais déjà regarder les nuages qui passent.

Je sais aussi rester en place.

Et je sais presque me taire.